Laboratory Manual

Programmable Logic Controllers

Hardware and Programming

by
Max Rabiee

Associate Professor of Electrical and Computer Engineering Technology,
University of Cincinnati

Contributing Editor:
Stephen Fardo
Professor, Department of Technology, Eastern Kentucky University

LogixPro PLC Simulation Software
by
Bill Simpson
Professor, Durham College Skills Training Centre, Whitby, Ontario

Publisher
The Goodheart-Willcox Company, Inc.
Tinley Park, Illinois

To my wife, for her love, patience, and support.

Introduction

This Laboratory Manual is designed to supplement your PLC training and works in conjunction with the *Programmable Logic Controllers—Hardware and Programming* textbook. These activities will lead you through a two-semester course in programmable logic controllers. The activities in this manual are written to give you hands-on experience practicing PLC programming and creating your own controller systems. The diagrams and activities begin with basic concepts and progress to more complex applications. The activities and diagrams in this manual are formulated on the Allen-Bradley Small Logic Controller (SLC 500) series programmable logic controllers and Rockwell Automation's *RSLogix 500* software.

These laboratory activities can be divided into four categories based on their level of complexity.

▶ Laboratory activities 1 through 17 are basic or beginning level PLC assignments.

▶ Laboratory activities 18 through 33 are intermediate level PLC assignments.

▶ Laboratory activities 34 through 41 are advanced level PLC assignments.

▶ Laboratory activities 42, 43, and 44 are PLC networking lab assignments.

Included with this Laboratory Manual is the *LogixPro* PLC simulation software. *LogixPro* is a tool to facilitate your learning of the fundamentals of RSLogix ladder logic programming. *LogixPro* will allow you to practice and develop your programming skills when and where you want. Note that *LogixPro* is not a replacement for RSLogix. There is no support for file exchange, nor is there support for communication with actual Allen-Bradley products. *LogixPro,* instead, provides a complete software based simulation solution. It is a solution designed specifically for training.

An extra special inclusion with the *LogixPro* software is the *ProSim-II Simulation* package that graphically simulates process equipment, such as batch mixing systems, traffic lights, and garage doors. The *ProSim-II Simulation* package gives you the synchronous and interactive experience of real industrial processes.

Using Your LogixPro Software

The first time you place the LogixPro CD into your disc drive, the LogixPro installation program should run automatically. To complete the installation, simply follow the prompts provided. This will install LogixPro on your PC. If the installation does not run automatically, you can start the installation program manually. Use Windows Explorer to locate the file titled **Install.exe** on the CD. You will find this file located in the root directory of the CD. Double clicking this file will start the installation.

In order to run LogixPro, you must first place the LogixPro CD into the computer's disc drive and ensure that the drive door is closed. LogixPro can then be started using the LogixPro icon located on the Windows desktop or the icon located at **Start | Programs | TheLearningPit | LogixPro**.

Future updates to LogixPro will be made available on the LogixPro Quick Update page at http://TheLearningPit.com. These free updates will allow you to add additional features to LogixPro as they become available. They may be downloaded directly from the Quick Update page.

The CD also comes with the program PSIM, an emulator for Allen-Bradley PLC/2 family PLCs. Double clicking on **simSetup.exe** found in the **PSIM** folder of the CD will invoke the self-extracting PSIM installation program. It will lead you through the installation and setup of PSIM.

Table of Contents

Intermediate Level PLC Assignments _____ 67

Advanced Level PLC Assignments _____ 117

PLC Networking Lab Assignments _____ 139

Materials, Equipment, and Software

The following list contains all the equipment and materials required to perform the activities in this manual. In some activities, different components can be substituted for the components listed here.

- ▶ Allen-Bradley fixed SLC 500 PLC with 1747-L20A processor or equivalent (2)
- ▶ Allen-Bradley SLC 503 PLC or equivalent
- ▶ Split-phase ac induction motors (2) (fractional horsepower)
- ▶ Single-pole, single-throw (SPST) switches (6)
- ▶ Normally open pushbuttons (3)
- ▶ Normally closed pushbutton
- ▶ Red, green, and white pilot lights
- ▶ Bell (6-volt)
- ▶ Scientific calculator

In addition to the hardware listed, these activities are designed around Rockwell Automation's *RSLogix 500* PLC programming software, the most popular software for programming the Allen-Bradley SLC 500 series PLC.

The *LogixPro* PLC simulation software included with this manual will allow you to simulate many of these activities. The *LogixPro* software will substitute for both the software and hardware components.

Number Systems

Name _____Date _____Instructor_____

Objectives:

This activity will familiarize you with the binary, octal, and hexadecimal number systems and allow you to practice converting to and from each of the common numbers systems.

Equipment:

▶ Scientific calculator

Procedure:

Answer the following questions in the space provided.

1. Match the letter of the following bases with the appropriate number system:

___ Hexadecimal   a. Base 10

___ Binary   b. Base 8

___ Octal   c. Base 16

___ Decimal   d. Base 2

2. Convert the following numbers to the specified number system.

   a. Convert from binary to decimal.

Binary number	Decimal equivalent
111	
1011	
101010	
10110011	
100110111110	

   b. Convert from decimal to binary.

Decimal number	Binary equivalent
14	
42	
162	
207	
459	

c. Convert from decimal to binary.

Decimal number	Binary equivalent
12.5	
323.625	
1678.00625	
1236.00075	
465.00025	

d. Convert from decimal to BCD.

Decimal number	BCD equivalent
56	
381	
1121	
4583	
6685	

e. Convert from BCD to decimal.

BCD number	Decimal equivalent
0110 0011	
0110 0011 0111 0110	
1000 1001 0100 0001	
0101 0000 1000 0101	
0011 0011 0010 0111	

f. Convert from decimal to octal.

Decimal number	Octal equivalent
7	
15	
88	
327	
1121	

g. Convert from octal to decimal.

Octal number	Decimal equivalent
6	
35	
77	
201	
4464	

h. Convert from decimal to hexadecimal.

Decimal number	Hexadecimal equivalent
8	
14	
79	
558	
1243	

i. Convert from hexadecimal to decimal.

Hexadecimal number	Decimal equivalent
11	
3C	
2A2	
BCF	
1B4C	

j. Convert from Gray code to hexadecimal.

Gray code number	Hexadecimal equivalent
1000 1001	
0011 0010	
1101 1110 1001	
1010 0011 0001	
1000 1100 1111 1110	

3. Convert each of the following binary numbers to decimal.

Binary number	Decimal equivalent
10011011	
01100101	
11011011	
01010101	

4. Convert each of the following numbers to decimal.

Number	Decimal equivalent
110011.1_2	
10010111.0011_{BCD}	
$1FEB.A_h$	
352.1_O	

Name _____

5. Convert the following numbers to binary.

Number	Binary equivalent
78.625_{10}	
112.25_{10}	
$ABC.0E_h$	
10010110.01110001_{BCD}	
761.15_O	

Basic PLC Terms and Data Files

Name _____ Date _____ Instructor _____

Objective:

This activity will familiarize you with programmable logic controller components and terminology. You will be able to describe the Allen-Bradley SLC 500 PLC data files.

Procedure:

Answer the following questions in the space provided.

1. How many input ports and output ports does your Fixed SLC 500 PLC lab station have? _____

2. A typical PLC device has four different components. Name these components.

   _____

   _____

   _____

   _____

3. Each PLC operational cycle has three separate parts. Name these parts.

   _____

   _____

   _____

4. Why is each input and output port connected to the CPU through an optoisolator chip such as the 4N32?

   _____

   _____

   _____

5. Describe the following programmable logic controller terms.

   a. Input image status: _____

   _____

   b. Output image status: _____

   _____

   c. CPU: _____

   _____

   d. Input/output (I/O) modules: _____

   _____

Name _____

6. Explain the function of the following data files in Allen-Bradley SLC 500 PLCs.

a. Bit (B3): _____

_____

b. Bit (B10): _____

_____

c. Control (R6): _____

_____

d. Counters (C5): _____

_____

e. Integer (N7): _____

_____

f. Status (S2): _____

_____

g. Timers (T4): _____

_____

Programming a PLC Station

CPLCPLCPLCPLCPLCPLCPL

Name _____ Date _____ Instructor_____

Objectives:

In this laboratory activity, you will connect input and output devices to PLC input/output ports. Then, you will create two PLC ladder logic diagrams and verify their operation.

Equipment:

▶ Allen-Bradley fixed SLC 500 PLC with 1747-L20A processor or equivalent
▶ Single-pole, single-throw (SPST) switches (2)
▶ Normally open pushbuttons (2)
▶ Red and green pilot lights
▶ Split-phase ac induction motor (fractional horsepower)

Procedure:

Activity 1

Examine the circuit in Figure 3-1. In this circuit, the green light turns on when switch number one (SW1) is pressed. The red light turns on when switches number one *and* two are both closed. In this activity, you will program the relay logic diagram for this illustration and then test the circuit.

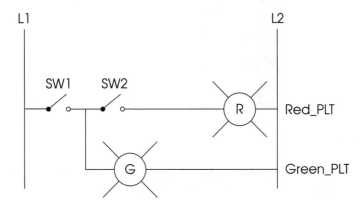

Figure 3-1

Name _____

Step 1. Assign the input and output terminals as indicated in the following.

Input device	**PLC input port address**
Switch one (SW1)	I:0/0
Switch two (SW2)	I:0/3
Output device	**PLC output port address**
Green pilot light (Green_PLT)	O:0/3
Red pilot light (Red_PLT)	O:0/4

Step 2. Examine Figure 3-2. This displays the PLC input/output port connection diagram for this lab assignment.

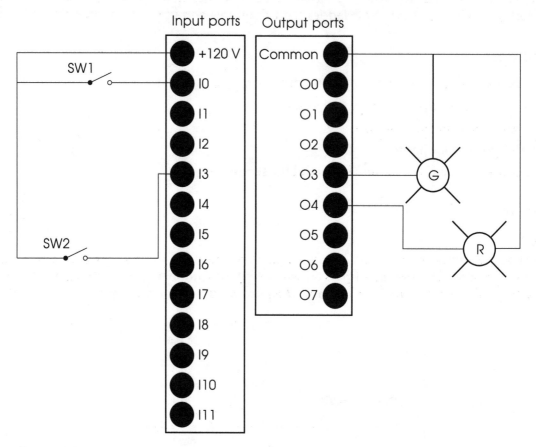

Figure 3-2

Step 3. Figure 3-3 displays the PLC ladder logic diagram for Activity 1. Using Rockwell RSLogix 500 software, create the PLC ladder logic diagram displayed in this figure.

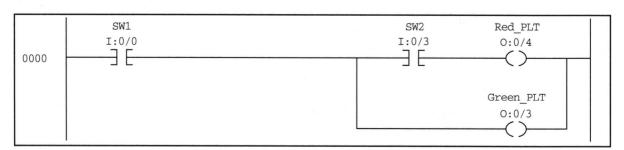

Figure 3-3

Name _____

Step 4. Download the PLC ladder logic diagram into the PLC station. Place the PLC in the run/monitor mode.

Step 5. Demonstrate your working PLC system for your instructor. Approval: _____

Activity 2

Figure 3-4 displays a relay logic diagram. In this activity, you will explain the circuit's operation, create the ladder logic diagram, and then test it.

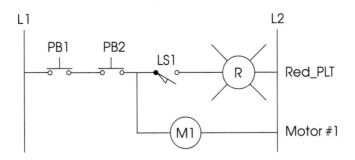

Figure 3-4

Step 1. Examine Figure 3-4 carefully. Describe the operation of the control system that is displayed.

_____

_____

_____

_____

Step 2. Assign the input and output terminals as indicated in the following.

Input device	PLC input port address
Pushbutton one (PB1)	I:0/1
Pushbutton two (PB2)	I:0/2
Limit switch one (LS1)	I:0/4
Output device	**PLC output port address**
Motor one (M1)	O:0/0
Red pilot light (Red_PLT)	O:0/4

Step 3. In the space that follows, draw the PLC input/output port connection for the I/O address assignments in Step 2. Then, complete the PLC I/O connection on your PLC lab station.

Name _____

Step 4. Use Rockwell RSLogix 500 software to create the PLC ladder logic diagram for the relay logic diagram displayed in Figure 3-4. Draw the PLC ladder logic diagram in the space that follows.

Step 5. Download the PLC ladder logic diagram into the PLC station. Place the PLC in the run/monitor mode.

Step 6. Demonstrate your working PLC system for your instructor. Approval: _____

PLC Output Contacts

Name _____ Date _____ Instructor_____

Objective:

In this laboratory activity, you will learn to use PLC coils and contacts. You will create PLC ladder logic diagrams that utilize contacts to seal output ports.

Equipment:

▶ Allen-Bradley fixed SLC 500 PLC with 1747-L20A processor or equivalent
▶ Single-pole, single-throw (SPST) switches (2)
▶ Normally closed pushbutton
▶ Red and green pilot lights
▶ Split-phase ac induction motor (fractional horsepower)

Procedure:

Activity 1

Figure 4-1 displays a relay logic diagram. In this activity, you will explain the circuit's operation, create the ladder logic diagram, and then test it.

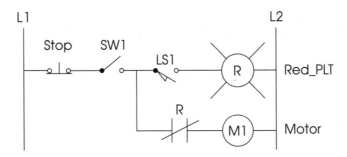

Figure 4-1

Step 1. Examine Figure 4-1 carefully. Describe the operation of the control system that is displayed.

_____

_____

_____

_____

Name _____

Step 2. Assign the input and output terminals as indicated in the following.

Input device	PLC input port address
Switch one (SW1)	I:0/0
Stop pushbutton (Stop)	I:0/1
Limit switch one (LS1)	I:0/3

Output device	PLC output port address
Motor one (M1)	O:0/0
Red pilot light (Red_PLT)	O:0/4

Step 3. In the space that follows, draw the PLC input/output port connection for the I/O address assignments in Step 2. Complete the PLC I/O connection on your PLC lab station.

Step 4. Use Rockwell RSLogix 500 software to create the PLC ladder logic diagram for the relay logic diagram displayed in Figure 4-1. Draw the PLC ladder logic diagram in the space that follows.

Step 5. Download the PLC ladder logic diagram into the PLC station. Place the PLC in the run/monitor mode.

Step 6. Demonstrate your working PLC system for your instructor. Approval: _____

Name _____

Activity 2

Figure 4-2 displays another relay logic diagram. In this activity, you will explain the circuit's operation, create the ladder logic diagram, and then test it.

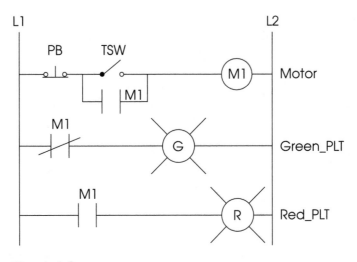

Figure 4-2

Step 1. Examine Figure 4-2 carefully. Describe the operation of the control system displayed.

_____

_____

_____

_____

Step 2. Assign the input and output terminals as indicated in the following.

Input device	PLC input port address
Pushbutton (PB)	I:0/1
Thermostat (TSW)	I:0/3

Output device	PLC output port address
Motor one (M1)	O:0/0
Green pilot light (Green_PLT)	O:0/3
Red pilot light (Red_PLT)	O:0/4

Name _____

Step 3. In the space that follows, draw the PLC input/output port connection for the I/O address assignments in Step 2. Complete the PLC I/O connection on your PLC lab station.

Step 4. Use Rockwell RSLogix 500 software to create the PLC ladder logic diagram for the relay logic diagram displayed in Figure 4-2. Draw the PLC ladder logic diagram in the space that follows.

Step 5. Download the PLC ladder logic diagram into the PLC station. Place the PLC in the run/monitor mode.

Step 6. Demonstrate your working PLC system for your instructor. Approval: _____

Internal PLC Relays and Contacts

Name _____ Date _____ Instructor_____

Objective:

In this activity, you will utilize normally open and normally closed contacts associated with PLC output devices. You will create two PLC ladder logic diagrams and verify their operation.

Equipment:

- Allen-Bradley fixed SLC 500 PLC with 1747-L20A processor or equivalent
- Single-pole, single-throw (SPST) switches (4)
- Normally closed pushbutton
- Red pilot light
- Bell (6-volt)
- Split-phase ac induction motor (fractional horsepower)

Procedure:

Activity 1

Figure 5-1 displays a relay logic diagram. In this activity, you will explain the circuit's operation, create the ladder logic diagram, and then test it.

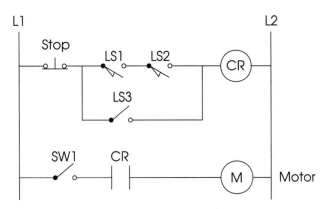

Figure 5-1

Step 1. Examine Figure 5-1 carefully. Describe the operation of the control system displayed.

_____

_____

_____

_____

_____

Name _____

Step 2. Assign the input and output terminals as illustrated in the following.

Input device	PLC input port address
Switch one (SW1)	I:0/0
Stop pushbutton (Stop)	I:0/1
Limit switch one (LS1)	I:0/3
Limit switch two (LS2)	I:0/4
Limit switch three (LS3)	I:0/5
Output device	**PLC output port address**
Motor (M)	O:0/0

Step 3. In the space that follows, draw the PLC input/output port connection for the I/O address assignments in Step 2. Complete the PLC I/O connection on your PLC lab station.

Step 4. Use the Rockwell RSLogix 500 software to create the PLC ladder logic diagram for the relay logic diagram displayed in Figure 5-1. Draw the PLC ladder logic diagram in the space that follows.

Name _____

Step 5. Download the PLC ladder logic diagram into the PLC station. Place the PLC in the run/monitor mode.

Step 6. Demonstrate your working PLC system for your instructor. Approval: _____

Activity 2

Figure 5-2 displays another relay logic diagram. In this activity, you will explain the circuit's operation, create the ladder logic diagram, and then test it.

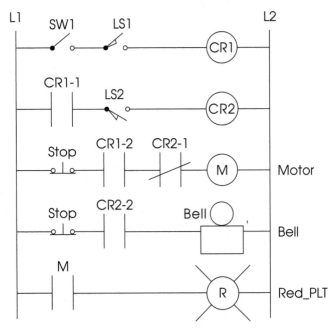

Figure 5-2

Step 1. Examine Figure 5-2 carefully. Describe the operation of the control system displayed.

_____

_____

_____

_____

_____

Step 2. Assign the input and output terminals as illustrated in the following.

Input device	PLC input port address
Switch one (SW1)	I:0/0
Stop pushbutton (Stop)	I:0/1
Limit switch one (LS1)	I:0/3
Limit switch two (LS2)	I:0/4
Output device	**PLC output port address**
Motor (M)	O:0/0
Bell	O:0/1
Red pilot light (Red_PLT)	O:0/4

Step 3. In the space that follows, draw the PLC input/output port connection for the I/O address assignments in Step 2. Complete the PLC I/O connection on your PLC lab station.

Step 4. Use the Rockwell RSLogix 500 software to create the PLC ladder logic diagram for the relay logic diagram displayed in Figure 5-2. Draw the PLC ladder logic diagram in the space that follows.

Step 5. Download the PLC ladder logic diagram into the PLC station. Place the PLC in the run/monitor mode.

Step 6. Demonstrate your working PLC system for your instructor. Approval: _____

Sealed Outputs

Name _____ Date _____ Instructor _____

Objective:

In this activity, you will learn how to use contacts to seal (lock) motors for continuous operation. Two PLC ladder logic diagrams will illustrate that motors can turn on and off with output and/or internal contacts.

Equipment:

▶ Allen-Bradley fixed SLC 500 PLC with 1747-L20A processor or equivalent
▶ Normally open pushbutton (2)
▶ Normally closed pushbutton
▶ Single-pole, single-throw (SPST) switch
▶ Red, green, and white pilot lights
▶ Split-phase ac induction motors (2) (fractional horsepower)

Procedure:

Activity 1

Figure 6-1 displays a relay logic diagram. In this activity, you will explain the circuit's operation, create the ladder logic diagram, and then test it.

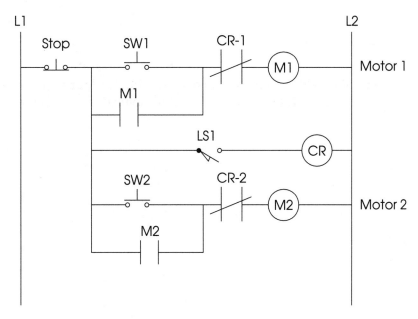

Figure 6-1

Name _____

Step 1. Examine Figure 6-1 carefully. Describe the operation of the control system displayed.

_____

_____

_____

_____

Step 2. Assign the input and output terminals as illustrated in the following.

Input device	PLC input port address
Switch one (SW1)	I:0/0
Stop pushbutton (Stop)	I:0/1
Limit switch one (LS1)	I:0/4
Switch two (SW2)	I:0/5

Output device	PLC output port address
Motor one (M1)	O:0/0
Motor two (M2)	O:0/5

Step 3. In the space that follows, draw the PLC input/output port connection for the I/O address assignments in Step 2. Complete the PLC I/O connection on your PLC lab station.

Step 4. Use the Rockwell RSLogix 500 software to create the PLC ladder logic diagram for the relay logic diagram displayed in Figure 6-1. Draw the PLC ladder logic diagram in the space that follows.

Name _____

Step 5. Download the PLC ladder logic diagram into the PLC station. Place the PLC in the run/monitor mode.

Step 6. Demonstrate your working PLC system for your instructor. Approval: _____

Activity 2

   Figure 6-2 displays another relay logic diagram. In this activity, you will explain the circuit's operation, create the ladder logic diagram, and then test it.

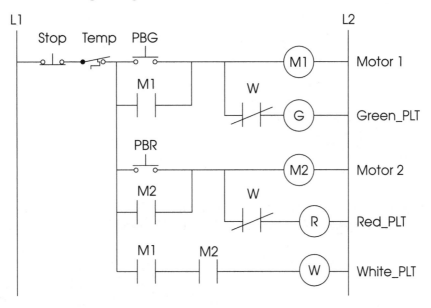

Figure 6-2

Step 1. Examine Figure 6-2 carefully. Describe the operation of the control system displayed.

_____

_____

_____

_____

_____

Step 2. Assign the input and output terminals as illustrated in the following.

Input device	PLC input port address
Stop pushbutton (Stop)	I:0/0
Green pushbutton (PBG)	I:0/1
Red pushbutton (PBR)	I:0/2
Thermostat (Temp)	I:0/3
Output device	**PLC output port address**
Motor one (M1)	O:0/0
White pilot light (White_PLT)	O:0/2
Green pilot light (Green_PLT)	O:0/3
Red pilot light (Red_PLT)	O:0/4
Motor two (M2)	O:0/5

Name _____

Step 3. In the space that follows, draw the PLC input/output port connection for the I/O address assignments in Step 2. Complete the PLC I/O connection on your PLC lab station.

Step 4. Use the Rockwell RSLogix 500 software to create the PLC ladder logic diagram for the relay logic diagram displayed in Figure 6-2. Draw the PLC ladder logic diagram in the space that follows.

Step 5. Download the PLC ladder logic diagram into the PLC station. Place the PLC in the run/monitor mode.

Step 6. Demonstrate your working PLC system for your instructor. Approval: _____

Latch/Unlatch Instructions

Name _____ Date _____ Instructor _____

Objective:

In this activity, you will learn how to use the latch and unlatch functions in PLC ladder logic diagrams. You will create two PLC ladder logic diagrams utilizing the latch and unlatch functions.

Equipment:

▶ Allen-Bradley fixed SLC 500 PLC with 1747-120A processor or equivalent
▶ Single-pole, single-throw switches (2)
▶ Normally open pushbuttons (2)
▶ Red, green, and white pilot lights

Procedure:

Activity 1

Figure 7-1 displays a relay logic diagram using the latch and unlatch functions. In this activity, you will explain the circuit's operation, create the ladder logic diagram, and then test it.

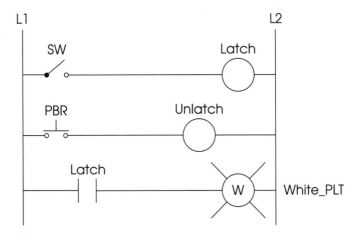

Figure 7-1

Step 1. Examine Figure 7-1 carefully. Describe the operation of the control system displayed.

_____

_____

_____

_____

_____

Name _____

Step 2. Assign the input and output terminals as illustrated in the following.

Input device	PLC input port address
Switch (SW)	I:0/0
Red pushbutton (PBR)	I:0/2
Output device	**PLC output port address**
White pilot light (White_PLT)	O:0/2

Step 3. In the space that follows, draw the PLC input/output port connection for the I/O address assignments in Step 2. Then, complete the PLC I/O connection on your PLC lab station.

Step 4. Use the Rockwell RSLogix 500 software to create the PLC ladder logic diagram for the relay logic diagram displayed in Figure 7-1. Draw the PLC ladder logic diagram in the following space.

Step 5. Download the PLC ladder logic diagram into the PLC station. Place the PLC in the run/monitor mode.

Step 6. Demonstrate your working PLC system for your instructor. Approval: _____

Name _____

Figure 7-2 displays another relay logic diagram using the latch and unlatch functions. In this activity, you will explain the circuit's operation, create the ladder logic diagram, and then test it.

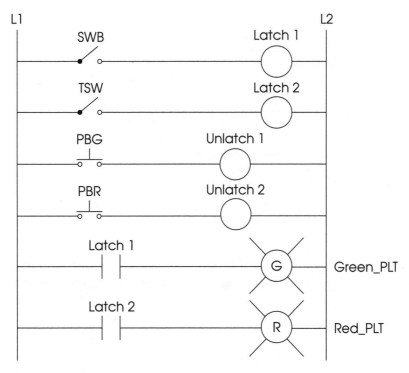

Figure 7-2

Step 1. Examine Figure 7-2 carefully. Describe the operation of the control system displayed.

_____

_____

_____

_____

_____

_____

Step 2. Assign the input and output terminals as illustrated in the following.

Input device	PLC input port address
Black switch (SWB)	I:0/0
Green pushbutton (PBG)	I:0/1
Red pushbutton (PBR)	I:0/2
Thermostat (TSW)	I:0/3
Output device	**PLC output port address**
Green pilot light (Green_PLT)	O:0/3
Red pilot light (Red_PLT)	O:0/4

Name _____

Step 3. In the space that follows, draw the PLC input/output port connection for the I/O address assignments in Step 2. Then, complete the PLC I/O connection on your PLC lab station.

Step 4. Use the Rockwell RSLogix 500 software to create the PLC ladder logic diagram for the relay logic diagram displayed in Figure 7-2. Draw the PLC ladder logic diagram in the following space.

Step 5. Download the PLC ladder logic diagram into the PLC station. Place the PLC in the run/monitor mode.

Step 6. Demonstrate your working PLC system for your instructor. Approval: _____

Control Problems (1)

Name _____ Date _____ Instructor _____

Objectives:

In this activity, you will learn how to create relay logic diagrams from problem descriptions. Then, you will create PLC ladder logic diagrams and verify their operation.

Equipment:

▶ Allen-Bradley fixed SLC 500 PLC with 1747-L20A processor or equivalent
▶ Single-pole, single-throw (SPST) switches (2)
▶ Normally open pushbuttons (2)
▶ Red, green, and white pilot lights
▶ Split-phase ac induction motors (2) (fractional horsepower)

Procedure:

Activity 1

Draw and then generate a PLC ladder diagram for a circuit that carries out the following control operations.

a. When switch one (SW1) is closed, the green light turns on.

b. When switch two (SW2) is closed, the yellow light turns on.

c. When both SW1 and SW2 are closed, the green and yellow lights are off, and the red light turns on.

Step 1. Draw the relay logic diagram.

Name _____

Step 2. Assign the input and output terminals.

<u>**Input device**</u>   <u>**PLC input port address**</u>

<u>**Output device**</u>   <u>**PLC output port address**</u>

Step 3. In the space that follows, draw the PLC input/output port connection for the I/O address assignments in Step 2. Then, complete the PLC I/O connection on your PLC lab station.

Step 4. Use the Rockwell RSLogix 500 software to create the PLC ladder logic diagram for the relay logic diagram in Step 1. Draw the PLC ladder logic diagram in the following space.

Name _____

Step 5. Download the PLC ladder logic diagram into the PLC station. Place the PLC in the run/monitor mode.

Step 6. Demonstrate your working PLC system for your instructor. Approval: _____

Activity 2

Draw and then generate a PLC ladder diagram for a circuit that carries out the following control operations.

    a. The black switch (SWB) is the emergency stop switch.

    b. When the red pushbutton (PBR) is pressed, the red light and motor number one are energized. They will stay on until SWB is opened.

    c. When the green pushbutton (PBG) is closed, both the white and green lights come on and both motors will run. They will stay on until SWB switch is opened.

Step 1. Draw the relay logic diagram.

Step 2. Assign the input and output terminals.

       Input device   **PLC input port address**

       Output device   **PLC output port address**

Name _____

Step 3. In the space that follows, draw the PLC input/output port connection for the I/O address assignments in Step 2. Then, complete the PLC I/O connection on your PLC lab station.

Step 4. Use the Rockwell RSLogix 500 software to create the PLC ladder logic diagram for the relay logic diagram in Step 1. Draw the PLC ladder logic diagram in the following space.

Step 5. Download the PLC ladder logic diagram into the PLC station. Place the PLC in the run/monitor mode.

Step 6. Demonstrate your working PLC system for your instructor. Approval: _____

Control Problems (2)

Name _____ Date _____ Instructor_____

Objectives:

In this activity, you will practice reading control problem descriptions and create their relay logic diagrams. Then, you will create PLC ladder logic diagrams and verify the relay logic diagram.

Equipment:

▶ Allen-Bradley fixed SLC 500 PLC with 1747-L20A processor or equivalent
▶ Single-pole, single-throw (SPST) switches (2)
▶ Normally open pushbuttons (2)
▶ Red, green, and white pilot lights
▶ Split-phase ac induction motors (2) (fractional horsepower)

Procedure:

Activity 1

Draw and then generate a PLC ladder diagram for a circuit that carries out the following control operations.

a. When the red pushbutton (PBR) is pressed, the white light and motor number one are energized and stay on.

b. When the black switch (SWB) is closed, both the white and green light come on and both motors run.

Step 1. Draw the relay logic diagram.

Step 2. Assign the input and output terminals.

<u>**Input device**</u>   <u>**PLC input port address**</u>

<u>**Output device**</u>   <u>**PLC output port address**</u>

Step 3. In the space that follows, draw the PLC input/output port connection for the I/O address assignments in Step 2. Then, complete the PLC I/O connection on your PLC lab station.

Step 4. Use the Rockwell RSLogix 500 software to create the PLC ladder logic diagram for the relay logic diagram in Step 1. Draw the PLC ladder logic diagram in the following space.

Step 5. Download the PLC ladder logic diagram into the PLC station. Place the PLC in the run/monitor mode.

Step 6. Demonstrate your working PLC system for your instructor. Approval: _____

Activity 2

Draw and then generate a PLC ladder diagram for a circuit that carries out the following control operations.

a. The black switch (SWB) is the master start/stop switch.

b. When the red pushbutton (PBR) is pressed once, both motors turn on. They run continuously.

c. If you close the thermostat switch (TSW), and press the green pushbutton (PBG) once, motor number one runs continuously.

d. When the thermostat switch is open, motor number one runs as long as the green pushbutton is pressed. This means that motor number one is in the jog mode. When motor number one is in the jog mode, the white pilot light (White_PLT) should be on.

Step 1. Draw the relay logic diagram.

Step 2. Assign the input and output terminals.

Input device   **PLC input port address**

Output device   **PLC output port address**

Step 3. In the space that follows, draw the PLC input/output port connection for the I/O address assignments in Step 2. Then, complete the PLC I/O connection on your PLC lab station.

Step 4. Use the Rockwell RSLogix 500 software to create the PLC ladder logic diagram for the relay logic diagram in Step 1. Draw the PLC ladder logic diagram in the following space.

Step 5. Download the PLC ladder logic diagram into the PLC station. Place the PLC in the run/monitor mode.

Step 6. Demonstrate your working PLC system for your instructor. Approval: _____

Using PLC Force Functions (1)

Name _____ Date _____ Instructor _____

Objectives:

In this activity, you will create PLC ladder logic diagrams and verify their operations. Then, you will use force functions to turn input and output ports on and off.

Equipment:

▶ Normally closed pushbutton
▶ Normally open pushbuttons (2)
▶ Split-phase ac induction motors (2) (fractional horsepower)

Procedure:

Activity 1

In the control system displayed in Figure 10-1, once the start pushbutton is pressed, the motor energizes and the relay contact M will close. The motor will run until the stop switch is opened.

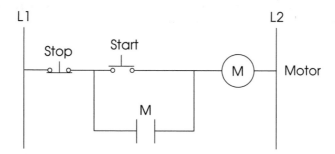

Figure 10-1

Step 1. Assign PLC input/output ports to the devices. Make the proper connections, and program your PLC to carry out the logic shown in Figure 10-1.

Step 2. Use the Rockwell RSLogix 500 software to create the PLC ladder logic diagram. Draw the PLC ladder logic diagram in the space that follows.

Name _____

Step 3. Download the PLC ladder logic diagram into the PLC station. Place the PLC in the run/monitor mode. Use the *force function* to carry out the operation.

Step 4. Demonstrate your working PLC system for your instructor. Approval: _____

Activity 2

In the following example, motor number one (M1) will run when switch number one (SW1) is closed, and motor number two (M2) will run when switch number two (SW2) is closed. Once either motor starts, it will run until the corresponding stop switch is opened.

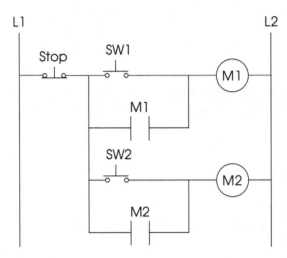

Figure 10-2

Step 1. Assign PLC input/output ports to the devices. Make the proper connections, and program your PLC to carry out the logic shown in Figure 10-2.

Step 2. Use the Rockwell RSLogix 500 software to create the PLC ladder logic diagram. Draw the PLC ladder logic diagram in the space that follows.

Step 3. Download the PLC ladder logic diagram into the PLC station. Place the PLC in the run/monitor mode. Use the *force function* to carry out the operation.

Step 4. Demonstrate your working PLC system for your instructor. Approval: _____

Name _____ Date _____ Instructor_____

Objectives:

In the first activity, you will create the PLC ladder logic diagram for a relay logic diagram. Then, you will verify the operation of PLC ladder logic diagram using the force function. In the second problem, you will create the relay logic and the PLC ladder logic diagram for a control problem. Then, you will verify the operation of PLC ladder logic diagram using the force function.

Equipment:

- Single-pole, single-throw (SPST) switch
- Normally closed pushbutton
- Normally open pushbuttons (2)
- Red, green, and white pilot lights
- Split-phase ac motors (2) (fractional horsepower)

Procedure:

Activity 1

In the following control system, when motor number one (M1) runs, the green light (G) light is on. When motor number two (M2) runs, the white light (W) is on. When both motors are running, only the red light (R) is on. Once the motors start running, the only way they are stopped is by either opening the stop switch or tripping the temperature switch. The temperature switch can be represented by the thermostat on the PLC workstation.

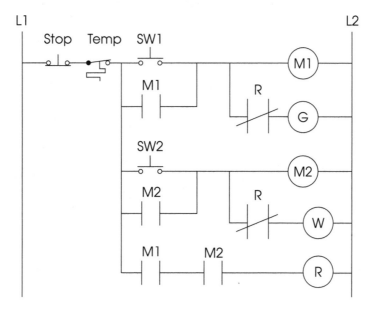

Figure 11-1

Step 1. Assign PLC input/output ports to the devices. Make the proper connections, and program your PLC to carry out the logic from Figure 11-1.

Step 2. Use the Rockwell RSLogix 500 software to create the PLC ladder logic diagram. Draw the PLC ladder logic diagram in the space that follows.

Step 3. Download the PLC ladder logic diagram into the PLC station. Place the PLC in the run/monitor mode. Use the *force function* to carry out the operation.

Step 4. Demonstrate your working PLC system for your instructor. Approval: _____

Activity 2

Draw the relay diagram and then create a circuit that operates as follows.

a. The black switch (SWB) is the master start/stop switch.

b. Pressing the red pushbutton (PBR) once turns both motors (M1 and M2) on. They will run continuously.

c. Pressing the green pushbutton (PBG) only turns on motor number two. Motor number two runs only if PBG is pressed.

Step 1. Draw the relay logic diagram.

Step 2. Assign PLC input/output ports to the devices. Make the proper connections and program your PLC to carry out the logic diagrammed in Step 1.

Step 3. Use the Rockwell RSLogix 500 software to create the PLC ladder logic diagram. Draw the PLC ladder logic diagram in the space that follows.

Step 4. Download the PLC ladder logic diagram into the PLC station. Place the PLC in the run/monitor mode. Use the *force function* to carry out the operation.

Step 5. Demonstrate your working PLC system for your instructor. Approval: _____

Programming Logic Gates on a PLC

Name _____ Date _____ Instructor _____

Objectives:

In this activity, you will practice converting logic gate circuits into ladder logic diagrams. You will then verify the operation of the ladder logic diagrams.

Equipment:

- Normally open pushbuttons (3)
- Pilot light

Procedure:

Activity 1

Using switches and the red light on the PLC station, implement the following logic gates.

- AND gate
- OR gate
- NAND gate
- NOR gate
- XOR gate
- XNOR gate

Step 1. Draw the gate symbols, write the truth tables, and draw the corresponding relay logic diagrams for the following gates.

Note: Assume that an open switch represents logic low while a closed switch represents a logic high.

<u>**AND gate**</u>   <u>**OR gate**</u>

NAND gate   **NOR gate**

XOR gate   **XNOR gate**

Step 2. Assign PLC input/output ports to the devices. Make the proper connections, and program your PLC to carry out the logic shown in the figures from Step 1.

Step 3. Use the Rockwell RSLogix 500 software to create the PLC ladder logic diagrams. Draw the PLC ladder logic diagrams in the space that follows.

Name _____

Step 4. Download the PLC ladder logic diagram into the PLC station. Place the PLC in the run/monitor mode.

Step 5. Demonstrate your working PLC system for your instructor. Approval: _____

Activity 2

Draw the relay logic diagram, PLC ladder diagram, and then create the following logic gate circuit.

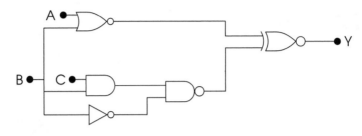

Figure 12-1

Step 1. Draw the relay logic diagram.

Step 2. Assign PLC input/output ports to the devices. Make the proper connections and program your PLC to carry out the logic diagrammed in Step 1.

Step 3. Use the Rockwell RSLogix 500 software to create the PLC ladder logic diagram. Draw the PLC ladder logic diagram in the space that follows.

Name _____

Step 4. Download the PLC ladder logic diagram into the PLC station. Place the PLC in the run/monitor mode.

Step 5. Demonstrate your working PLC system for your instructor. Approval: _____

Using a Truth Table Logic Gate Circuit to Program a PLC

Name _____Date _____Instructor_____

Objectives:

In this activity, you will learn how to use truth tables to create PLC ladder logic diagrams. You will also use logic gate circuits to create ladder logic diagrams. You will then verify operations of their ladder logic diagrams.

Equipment:

▶ Single-pole, single-throw (SPST) switches (5)
▶ Red, green, and white pilot lights

Procedure:

Activity 1

The following truth table can be used to generate a combinational logic circuit. Use this truth table to generate Boolean expressions. Use the Boolean expressions to generate a ladder logic diagram and then create the circuit.

A	B	C	Y1	Y2	Y3
0	0	0	0	0	1
0	0	1	0	1	1
0	1	0	0	1	1
0	1	1	1	0	0
1	0	0	0	1	1
1	0	1	1	0	0
1	1	0	1	0	0
1	1	1	1	0	0

Step 1. Create the Boolean expressions for the outputs as set in the truth table. Reduce the expressions as much as possible.

Name _____

Step 2. Assign PLC input/output ports to the devices. Make the proper connections, and program your PLC to carry out the logic. Assume that:

▶ Logic low = Open switch
▶ Logic high = Closed switch
▶ Y1 = Green light
▶ Y2 = White light
▶ Y3 = Red light

Use the following circuit description.

a. If there are no parts, turn the red light on.

b. If there are at least two parts, turn the green light on.

c. If there is one part, turn both the white and the red lights on.

Step 3. Use the Rockwell RSLogix 500 software to create the PLC ladder logic diagrams. Draw the PLC ladder logic diagrams in the space that follows.

Step 4. Download the PLC ladder logic diagram into the PLC station. Place the PLC in the run/monitor mode.

Step 5. Demonstrate your working PLC system for your instructor. Approval: _____

Activity 2

Examine the following logic gate circuit. Use this circuit to draw a logic ladder diagram and then create the circuit.

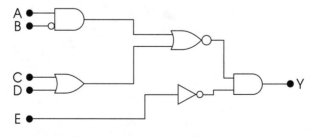

Figure 13-1

Name _____

Step 1. Assign PLC input/output ports to the devices. Make the proper connections, and program your PLC to carry out the logic from Figure 13-1.

Step 2. Use the Rockwell RSLogix 500 software to create the PLC ladder logic diagram. Draw the PLC ladder logic diagram in the space that follows.

Step 3. Download the PLC ladder logic diagram into the PLC station. Place the PLC in the run/monitor mode.

Step 4. Demonstrate your working PLC system for your instructor. Approval: _____

Converting Relay Logic to Logic Gate Circuits

Name _____ Date _____ Instructor _____

Objective:

In this activity, you will practice converting PLC ladder logic diagrams to logic gate diagrams.

Equipment:

▶ Single-pole, single-throw (SPST) switches (5)
▶ Red and green pilot lights
▶ Split-phase ac induction motor (fractional horsepower)

Procedure:

Activity 1

Convert the following PLC ladder diagram to a logic gate diagram.

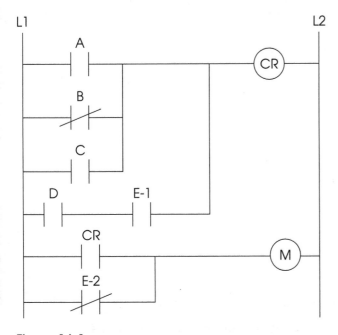

Figure 14-1

Step 1. Write out the Boolean expression created by the ladder diagram beside Figure 14-1.

Step 2. Assign PLC input/output ports to the devices. Make the proper I/O connections on the PLC. Use the Rockwell RSLogix 500 software to create the PLC ladder logic diagrams.

Step 3. Download the PLC ladder logic diagram into the PLC station. Place the PLC in the run/monitor mode.

Step 4. Demonstrate your working PLC system for your instructor. Approval: _____

Step 5. Draw the logic gate diagram in the following space.

Activity 2

Convert the following PLC ladder diagram to a logic gate diagram.

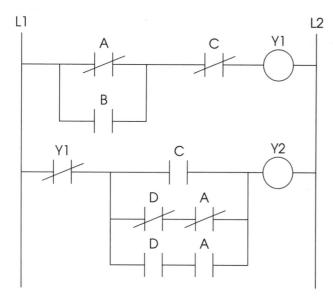

Figure 14-2

Step 1. Write out the Boolean expression created by the ladder diagram beside Figure 14-2.

Step 2. Assign PLC input/output ports to the devices. Make the proper I/O connections on the PLC. Use the Rockwell RSLogix 500 software to create the PLC ladder logic diagrams.

Step 3. Download the PLC ladder logic diagram into the PLC station. Place the PLC in the run/monitor mode.

Step 4. Demonstrate your working PLC system for your instructor. Approval: _____

Step 5. Draw the logic gate diagram in the following space.

Programming Boolean Expressions on PLCs (1)

Name _____ Date _____ Instructor_____

Objective:

In this activity, you will practice creating PLC ladder logic diagram from Boolean expressions.

Equipment:

▶ Single-pole, single-throw (SPST) switches (2)
▶ Normally open pushbuttons (2)
▶ Red pilot light

Procedure:

Activity 1

Draw the relay logic diagram of the following Boolean expression and then program it on your PLC lab station.

$$Y = A'BCD + B'C + D'B + ABCD$$

Step 1. Draw the relay logic diagram for the Boolean expression.

Step 2. Assign PLC input/output ports to the devices. Make the proper connections, and program your PLC to carry out the logic from Step 1. Assume that:

▶ A = Black switch
▶ B = Green pushbutton
▶ C = Red pushbutton
▶ D = Thermostat
▶ Y = Red pilot light

Name _____

Step 3. Use the Rockwell RSLogix 500 software to create the PLC ladder logic diagrams. Download the PLC ladder logic diagram into the PLC station. Place the PLC in the run/monitor mode.

Step 4. Demonstrate your working PLC system for your instructor. Approval: _____

Activity 2

Draw the relay logic diagram of the following Boolean expression and then program it on your PLC lab station.

$$Y = (A + BC)(C + AD + B)$$

Step 1. Draw the relay logic diagram for the Boolean expression.

Step 2. Assign PLC input/output ports to the devices. Make the proper connections, and program your PLC to carry out the logic from Step 1. Assume that:

▶ A = Black switch
▶ B = Green pushbutton
▶ C = Red pushbutton
▶ D = Thermostat
▶ Y = Red pilot light

Step 3. Use the Rockwell RSLogix 500 software to create the PLC ladder logic diagrams. Download the PLC ladder logic diagram into the PLC station. Place the PLC in the run/monitor mode.

Step 4. Demonstrate your working PLC system for your instructor. Approval: _____

Programming Boolean Expressions on PLCs (2)

Lab Assignment

16

Name _____ Date _____ Instructor _____

Objectives:

In this activity, you will practice programming from Boolean expressions. In the first exercise, you will find the Boolean expression from the PLC ladder logic diagram. In the second exercise, you will create a PLC ladder logic diagram from a Boolean expression. You will also verify the operation of both ladder logic diagrams.

Equipment:

▶ Allen-Bradley fixed SLC 500 PLC or equivalent
▶ Single-pole, single-throw (SPST) switches (4)
▶ Normally open pushbuttons (2)
▶ Red pilot light

Procedure:

Activity 1

Program the following relay logic diagram on your PLC lab station and find its Boolean expression.

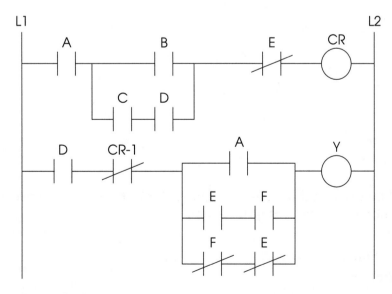

Figure 16-1

Step 1. Assign PLC input/output ports to the devices. Make the proper connections, and program your PLC to carry out the logic from Figure 16-1.

Step 2. Use the Rockwell RSLogix 500 software to create the PLC ladder logic diagrams. Download the PLC ladder logic diagram into the PLC station. Place the PLC in the run/monitor mode.

Name _____

Step 3. Demonstrate your working PLC system for your instructor. Approval: _____

Step 4. Find the Boolean expression for the relay logic diagram.

Activity 2

Draw the relay logic diagram of the following Boolean expression and then program it on your PLC lab station.

$$Y = A + C + B'D$$

Step 1. Draw the relay logic diagram for the Boolean expression.

Step 2. Assign PLC input/output ports to the devices. Make the proper connections, and program your PLC to carry out the logic from Step 1. Assume that:

▶ A = Black switch
▶ B = Green pushbutton
▶ C = Red pushbutton
▶ D = Thermostat
▶ Y = Red pilot light

Step 3. Use the Rockwell RSLogix 500 software to create the PLC ladder logic diagrams. Download the PLC ladder logic diagram into the PLC station. Place the PLC in the run/monitor mode.

Step 4. Demonstrate your working PLC system for your instructor. Approval: _____

Converting a Problem Description

Name _____ Date _____ Instructor _____

Objectives:

In this activity, you will practice creating logic gate circuits and PLC ladder logic diagrams from problem descriptions. Then, you will verify the operation of the PLC ladder logic diagrams.

Equipment:

- Allen-Bradley fixed SLC 500 PLC or equivalent
- Single-pole, single-throw (SPST) switches (4)
- Red and green pilot lights

Procedure:

Activity 1

Work from the following problem description.

Switch one (SW1) and switch two (SW2), plus either switch three (SW3) or switch four (SW4), must be on for the red pilot light to be on.

Step 1. Draw the truth table.

Name _____

Step 2. Find the Boolean expression and draw the logic gate circuit.

Step 3. Assign PLC input/output ports to the devices. Make the proper connections and program your PLC to carry out the logic.

Step 4. Use the Rockwell RSLogix 500 software to create the PLC ladder logic diagrams. Download the PLC ladder logic diagram into the PLC station. Place the PLC in the run/monitor mode.

Step 5. Demonstrate your working PLC system for your instructor. Approval: _____

Activity 2

Work from the following problem description.

For the green pilot light to be on, switch one (SW1) and switch four (SW4) must be off, and either switch two (SW2) or switch three (SW3) must be on.

Step 1. Draw the truth table.

Name _____

Step 2. Find the Boolean expression and draw the logic gate circuit.

Step 3. Assign PLC input/output ports to the devices. Make the proper connections and program your PLC to carry out the logic.

Step 4. Use the Rockwell RSLogix 500 software to create the PLC ladder logic diagrams. Download the PLC ladder logic diagram into the PLC station. Place the PLC in the run/monitor mode.

Step 5. Demonstrate your working PLC system for your instructor. Approval: _____

PLC Timer Functions (1)

Name _____ Date _____ Instructor_____

Objective:

In this activity, you will program nonretentive timers to control PLC output ports.

Equipment:

▶ Allen-Bradley fixed SLC 500 PLC or equivalent
▶ Single-pole, single-throw (SPST) switches (2)
▶ Red, green, and white pilot lights
▶ Split-phase ac induction motors (2) (fractional horsepower)

Procedure:

Review the following on the use of timer ON-delay and timer OFF-delay functions.

Timer ON-delay means that when the preset time has decreased to zero, the timer done coil energizes. The corresponding contact(s) then close or open.

Timer ON-delay (NO) contact   **Timer ON-delay (NC) contact**

Figure 18-1

Timer OFF-delay means that when the preset time has decreased to zero, the timer done coil de-energizes. The corresponding contact(s) then close or open.

Timer OFF-delay (NO) contact   **Timer OFF-delay (NC) contact**

Figure 18-2

In this activity, you will be programming your PLC station for a control circuit that carries out the following sequence of events.

  a. When SW2 is closed, the red pilot light turns on, motor number one (M1) starts running, and the bell sounds.

  b. After 10 seconds, M1 stops running and the white pilot light turns on.

  c. Fifteen seconds after the processes in Part b have been carried out, both the red and the white lights turn off, and the green light turns on.

d. Finally, five seconds after the processes in Part c have been carried out, both motors will start running.

e. If SW1 is opened, the process is halted.

Step 1. Draw the relay logic diagram for this circuit.

Step 2. Assign PLC input/output ports to the devices. Make the proper connections and program your PLC to carry out the logic diagrammed in Step 1.

Step 3. Use the Rockwell RSLogix 500 software to create the PLC ladder logic diagrams. Download the PLC ladder logic diagram into the PLC station. Place the PLC in the run/monitor mode.

Step 4. Demonstrate your working PLC system for your instructor. Approval: _____

PLC Timer Functions (2)

Name _____ Date _____ Instructor _____

Objective:

In this activity, you will complete two exercises that demonstrate how to create ladder logic diagram utilizing timer ON-delay functions.

Equipment:

- Allen-Bradley fixed SLC 500 PLC or equivalent
- Single-pole, single-throw (SPST) switch
- Normally open pushbutton
- Red, green, and white pilot lights
- Split-phase induction motors (2) (fractional horsepower)

Procedure:

Activity 1

In this activity, you will program your PLC station to produce a control circuit that carries out the following operations. When switch SW1 is closed, the red, white, and green pilot lights turn on and off every two seconds. That is, the red light comes on for two seconds and then goes off. Then the white light comes on for two seconds and goes off. Finally, the green light comes on for two seconds and turns off. This process should continue until switch SW1 is opened.

Step 1. Draw the relay logic diagram for this circuit.

Step 2. Assign PLC input/output ports to the devices. Make the proper connections and program your PLC to carry out the logic diagrammed in Step 1.

Step 3. Use the Rockwell RSLogix 500 software to create the PLC ladder logic diagrams. Download the PLC ladder logic diagram into the PLC station. Place the PLC in the run/monitor mode.

Step 4. Demonstrate your working PLC system for your instructor. Approval: _____

Activity 2

In this activity, you will program your PLC station to produce a control circuit that carries out the following operations. When the start pushbutton is depressed, motor number one (M1) turns on. After five seconds, motor number two (M2) turns on. Ten seconds after M2 turns on, the red pilot light should turn on. This process should continue until the master stop switch is opened.

Step 1. Draw the relay logic diagram for this circuit.

Step 2. Assign PLC input/output ports to the devices. Make the proper connections and program your PLC to carry out the logic diagrammed in Step 1.

Step 3. Use the Rockwell RSLogix 500 software to create the PLC ladder logic diagrams. Download the PLC ladder logic diagram into the PLC station. Place the PLC in the run/monitor mode.

Step 4. Demonstrate your working PLC system for your instructor. Approval: _____

PLC Timer Functions (3)

Name _____ Date _____ Instructor _____

Objectives:

In the first problem of this activity, you will use the timer ON-delay function to create a PLC ladder logic diagram. In the second problem, you will use the timer OFF-delay function to create a PLC ladder logic diagram. You will verify the operation of both PLC ladder logic diagrams on your PLC lab station.

Equipment:

▶ Allen-Bradley fixed SLC 500 PLC or equivalent
▶ Single-pole, single-throw (SPST) switches (2)
▶ Red, green, and white pilot lights
▶ Split-phase ac induction motors (2) (fractional horsepower)

Procedure:

Activity 1

In this problem, you will program your PLC station for a control circuit that carries out the following sequence of events to surface-harden steel plates in a factory.

    a. A normally open switch is closed to start the process. The green pilot light indicates the start of the process.

    b. When a limit switch is closed, motor number one (M1) runs for five seconds to lift the part. Use the thermostats on the PLC stations in the lab as limit switches.

    c. Next, the red light turns on for 10 seconds to indicate the induction heating process.

    d. After the red light has been on for 10 seconds, turn it off and turn motor number two (M2) on for eight seconds to spray cold water on the part.

    e. Two seconds after M2 shuts off, the white light should turn on.

Name _____

Step 1. Draw the relay logic diagram for this circuit.

Step 2. Assign PLC input/output ports to the devices. Make the proper connections and program your PLC to carry out the logic diagrammed in Step 1.

Step 3. Use the Rockwell RSLogix 500 software to create the PLC ladder logic diagrams. Download the PLC ladder logic diagram into the PLC station. Place the PLC in the run/monitor mode.

Step 4. Demonstrate your working PLC system for your instructor. Approval: _____

Activity 2

In this problem, you will program your PLC station using timer OFF-delay functions for a control circuit that carries out the following operations.

    a. SW1 is the master emergency switch that turns everything off.

    b. When SW2 is closed, the red pilot light turns on and the motor turns on.

    c. When SW2 is opened, the motor turns off immediately and the red pilot light remains on for another 20 seconds.

Name _____

Step 1. Draw the relay logic diagram for this circuit.

Step 2. Assign PLC input/output ports to the devices. Make the proper connections and program your PLC to carry out the logic diagrammed in Step 1.

Step 3. Use the Rockwell RSLogix 500 software to create the PLC ladder logic diagrams. Download the PLC ladder logic diagram into the PLC station. Place the PLC in the run/monitor mode.

Step 4. Demonstrate your working PLC system for your instructor. Approval: _____

Name _____ Date _____ Instructor_____

Objectives:

In this activity, you will use counter functions to create PLC ladder logic diagrams. Then, you will verify the operation of the PLC ladder logic diagrams on your PLC lab station.

Equipment:

- Allen-Bradley fixed SLC 500 PLC or equivalent
- Single-pole, single-throw (SPST) switch (2)
- Normally open pushbuttons (2)
- Red, green, and white pilot lights

Procedure:

Activity 1

In this problem, you will program your PLC station for a control circuit that carries out the following operations. A fan is to be turned on when counter A goes from 7 down to 0 and when either counter B goes up to 14 or counter C has gone from 14 down to 0. One switch resets the entire process.

Step 1. Draw the relay logic diagram for this circuit.

Step 2. Assign PLC input/output ports to the devices. Make the proper connections and program your PLC to carry out the logic diagrammed in Step 1.

Step 3. Use the Rockwell RSLogix 500 software to create the PLC ladder logic diagrams. Download the PLC ladder logic diagram into the PLC station. Place the PLC in the run/monitor mode.

Name _____

Step 4. Demonstrate your working PLC system for your instructor. Approval: _____

Activity 2

Using the PLC counter and retentive timer functions, program your PLC station using timer OFF-delay functions for a control circuit that carries out the following sequence of events.

    a. If the red pushbutton is pressed six times, the red light turns on.

    b. If the green pushbutton is pressed three times, the green light turns on.

    c. If the red pushbutton and the green pushbutton are pressed 12 times, only the white light turns on. (Note that as long as the total is 12, the white light should turn on. This means that the pressing combination does not matter.)

    d. Three timers should show how long each light has been on.

Step 1. Draw the relay logic diagram for this circuit.

Step 2. Assign PLC input/output ports to the devices. Make the proper connections and program your PLC to carry out the logic diagrammed in Step 1.

Step 3. Use the Rockwell RSLogix 500 software to create the PLC ladder logic diagrams. Download the PLC ladder logic diagram into the PLC station. Place the PLC in the run/monitor mode.

Step 4. Demonstrate your working PLC system for your instructor. Approval: _____

PLC Counter Functions (2)

Name _____ Date _____ Instructor_____

Objectives:

In this activity, you will use counter and timer functions to create PLC ladder logic diagrams. Then, you will verify the operation of your PLC ladder logic diagrams.

Equipment:

▶ Allen-Bradley fixed SLC 500 PLC or equivalent
▶ Single-pole, single-throw (SPST) switch
▶ Normally open pushbuttons (2)
▶ Red, green, and white pilot lights

Procedure:

Activity 1

In this activity, you will program your PLC station for a control circuit that carries out the following operations.

    a. Use the switch (SW1) to reset.

    b. If the green pushbutton is pressed once, the red and green lights turn on.

    c. If the green pushbutton is pressed twice, only the white light turns on.

Step 1. Draw the relay logic diagram for this circuit.

Step 2. Assign PLC input/output ports to the devices. Make the proper connections and program your PLC to carry out the logic diagrammed in Step 1.

Step 3. Use the Rockwell RSLogix 500 software to create the PLC ladder logic diagrams. Download the PLC ladder logic diagram into the PLC station. Place the PLC in the run/monitor mode.

Step 4. Demonstrate your working PLC system for your instructor. Approval: _____

Activity 2

In this activity, you will program your PLC station for a control circuit that carries out the following operations.

    a. Use the switch (SW1) to reset the system.

    b. If the green pushbutton and red pushbutton are each pressed three times, the red and green lights will turn on.

    c. The lights will stay on for only three (3) seconds.

Step 1. Draw the relay logic diagram for this circuit.

Step 2. Assign PLC input/output ports to the devices. Make the proper connections and program your PLC to carry out the logic diagrammed in Step 1.

Step 3. Use the Rockwell RSLogix 500 software to create the PLC ladder logic diagrams. Download the PLC ladder logic diagram into the PLC station. Place the PLC in the run/monitor mode.

Step 4. Demonstrate your working PLC system for your instructor. Approval: _____

PLC Counter Functions (3)

Name _____ Date _____ Instructor _____

Objectives:

In the first problem, you will use timer functions to create a PLC ladder logic diagram. In the second problem, you will use counter and timer functions to create a PLC ladder logic diagram. You will verify the operation of both ladder logic diagrams on your PLC lab station.

Equipment:

- Allen-Bradley fixed SLC 500 PLC or equivalent
- Single-pole, single-throw (SPST) switch
- Normally open pushbuttons (2)
- Green pilot light
- Bell (6-volt)
- Split-phase ac induction motors (2) (fractional horsepower)

Procedure:

Activity 1

Use the black switch (SWB) to reset. Close switch (TSW) to start the following sequence of events.

    a. Motor number one runs for three seconds.

    b. Then, motor number two runs for five seconds.

    c. Finally, the bell rings three times.

Step 1. Draw the relay logic diagram for this circuit.

Step 2. Assign PLC input/output ports to the devices. Make the proper connections and program your PLC to carry out the logic diagrammed in Step 1.

Step 3. Use the Rockwell RSLogix 500 software to create the PLC ladder logic diagrams. Download the PLC ladder logic diagram into the PLC station. Place the PLC in the run/monitor mode.

Step 4. Demonstrate your working PLC system for your instructor. Approval: _____

Activity 2

In this activity, you will program your PLC station for a control circuit that carries out the following operations. If counter number one, which is connected to pushbutton number one, counts five times and counter number two, which is connected to pushbutton number two, counts three times, then the green pilot light turns on for 10 seconds and the bell rings five times.

Step 1. Draw the relay logic diagram for this circuit.

Step 2. Assign PLC input/output ports to the devices. Make the proper connections and program your PLC to carry out the logic diagrammed in Step 1.

Step 3. Use the Rockwell RSLogix 500 software to create the PLC ladder logic diagrams. Download the PLC ladder logic diagram into the PLC station. Place the PLC in the run/monitor mode.

Step 4. Demonstrate your working PLC system for your instructor. Approval: _____

PLC Counter/Timer Functions (1)

Name _____Date _____Instructor_____

Objectives:

In the first problem, you will use timer OFF-delay functions to create a PLC ladder logic diagram. In the second problem, you will use counter and timer functions to create a PLC ladder logic diagram. You will also verify the operation of both ladder logic diagrams on your PLC lab station.

Equipment:

- ▶ Allen-Bradley fixed SLC 500 PLC or equivalent
- ▶ Single-pole, single-throw (SPST) switches (2)
- ▶ Normally open pushbuttons (2)
- ▶ Bell (6-volt)
- ▶ Red and green pilot lights
- ▶ Split-phase ac induction motors (2) (fractional horsepower)

Procedure:

Activity 1

Use the stop switch (SW) for reset. Close the thermostat (TSW) switch to start the following operations. The green lamp is the lubricating pump for the left motor and the red lamp is the lubricating pump for the right motor. When the motors are running, their lubricating pumps must be on. When the left motor stops, its lubricating pump should stay on for an additional ten seconds. When the right motor stops, its lubricating pump stays on only five seconds longer. In addition, whenever either of the lubricating pumps is on without its associated motor operating, the bell must sound repeatedly.

Name _____

Step 1. Draw the relay logic diagram for this circuit.

Step 2. Assign PLC input/output ports to the devices. Make the proper connections and program your PLC to carry out the logic diagrammed in Step 1.

Step 3. Use the Rockwell RSLogix 500 software to create the PLC ladder logic diagrams. Download the PLC ladder logic diagram into the PLC station. Place the PLC in the run/monitor mode.

Step 4. Demonstrate your working PLC system for your instructor. Approval: _____

Activity 2

In this activity, you will program your PLC station for a control circuit that carries out the following operations. If the green pushbutton (PBG) and/or the red pushbutton (PBR) are pressed ten times, the bell should sound once every second and the green light must blink every two seconds. If PBG is pressed eight times, the right motor should run and the red light should blink once every second. If PBR is pressed six times, the left motor should run and the white light must blink every three seconds.

Name _____

Step 1. Draw the relay logic diagram for this circuit.

Step 2. Assign PLC input/output ports to the devices. Make the proper connections and program your PLC to carry out the logic diagrammed in Step 1.

Step 3. Use the Rockwell RSLogix 500 software to create the PLC ladder logic diagrams. Download the PLC ladder logic diagram into the PLC station. Place the PLC in the run/monitor mode.

Step 4. Demonstrate your working PLC system for your instructor. Approval: _____

PLC Counter/Timer Functions (2)

Name _____Date _____Instructor_____

Objectives:

In these activities, you will use timer and counter functions to create two PLC ladder logic diagrams. Then, you will verify the operation of the PLC ladder logic diagrams.

Equipment:

- ▶ Allen-Bradley fixed SLC 500 PLC or equivalent
- ▶ Single-pole single-throw switch
- ▶ Normally open pushbuttons (2)
- ▶ Bell (6-volt)
- ▶ Red, green, and white pilot lights
- ▶ Split-phase ac induction motors (2) (fractional horsepower)

Procedure:

Activity 1

In this activity, you will program your PLC station for a control circuit that carries out the following operations. Black switch (SWB) is the main start/stop switch. When the green pushbutton is pressed, the following outputs will turn on with the specified time interval between them.

a. The left motor and green light turn on immediately.

b. The right motor and white light will turn on five seconds later.

c. Four seconds after the right motor has turned on, the bell will sound three times.

d. Finally, six seconds after the bell has finished ringing, all the outputs go off and the red light comes on.

Name _____

Step 1. Draw the relay logic diagram for this circuit.

Step 2. Assign PLC input/output ports to the devices. Make the proper connections and program your PLC to carry out the logic diagrammed in Step 1.

Step 3. Use the Rockwell RSLogix 500 software to create the PLC ladder logic diagrams. Download the PLC ladder logic diagram into the PLC station. Place the PLC in the run/monitor mode.

Step 4. Demonstrate your working PLC system for your instructor. Approval: _____

Activity 2

In this activity, you will program your PLC station for a control circuit that carries out the following events.

a. Press the red pushbutton (PBR) to flash the white pilot light (White_PLT) and the green pilot light (Green_PLT) six times within six seconds.

b. After the lights have been blinking, both motors should run for ten seconds. While the motors are running, the red pilot light should flash once every two seconds.

c. Finally, both motors and the red light should go off. Open the black switch (SWB) to reset the system.

Name _____

Step 1. Draw the relay logic diagram for this circuit.

Step 2. Assign PLC input/output ports to the devices. Make the proper connections and program your PLC to carry out the logic diagrammed in Step 1.

Step 3. Use the Rockwell RSLogix 500 software to create the PLC ladder logic diagrams. Download the PLC ladder logic diagram into the PLC station. Place the PLC in the run/monitor mode.

Step 4. Demonstrate your working PLC system for your instructor. Approval: _____

Programmable Logic Controllers Laboratory Manual

PLC Counter/Timer Functions (3)

Name _____ Date _____ Instructor_____

Objectives:

In these activities, you will use timer and counter functions to create two PLC ladder logic diagrams. Then, you will verify the operations of the PLC ladder logic diagrams.

Equipment:

- Allen-Bradley fixed SLC 500 PLC or equivalent
- Single-pole, single-throw (SPST) switch
- Normally open pushbuttons (2)
- Red, green, and white pilot lights
- Split-phase ac induction motors (2) (fractional horsepower)

Procedure:

Activity 1

In this activity, you will program your PLC station for a control circuit that carries out the following operations.

a. The black switch is the master reset switch.

b. If the green pushbutton is pressed four times and the red pushbutton is pressed twice, the white pilot light and the left motor turn on for five seconds.

c. If the green pushbutton is pressed five times and the red pushbutton is pressed three times, the green pilot light and the right motor turn on for 10 seconds.

d. If the green and/or red pushbuttons are pressed a total of 15 times, both motors run and both the white and green pilot lights turn on.

Step 1. Draw the relay logic diagram for this circuit.

Step 2. Assign PLC input/output ports to the devices. Make the proper connections and program your PLC to carry out the logic diagrammed in Step 1.

Step 3. Use the Rockwell RSLogix 500 software to create the PLC ladder logic diagrams. Download the PLC ladder logic diagram into the PLC station. Place the PLC in the run/monitor mode.

Step 4. Demonstrate your working PLC system for your instructor. Approval: _____

Activity 2

In this activity, you will program your PLC station for a control circuit that carries out the following operations.

    a. If the green pushbutton is pressed four times, the white pilot light and motor number one turn on for five seconds.

    b. If the green pushbutton is pressed five times, the green pilot light and motor number two turn on for 10 seconds.

    c. If the red pushbutton is pressed once, the red pilot light and both motors turn on for five seconds.

    d. Black switch (SWB) is used as a reset.

Name _____

Step 1. Draw the relay logic diagram for this circuit.

Step 2. Assign PLC input/output ports to the devices. Make the proper connections and program your PLC to carry out the logic diagrammed in Step 1.

Step 3. Use the Rockwell RSLogix 500 software to create the PLC ladder logic diagrams. Download the PLC ladder logic diagram into the PLC station. Place the PLC in the run/monitor mode.

Step 4. Demonstrate your working PLC system for your instructor. Approval: _____

PLC Counter/Timer Functions (4)

Name _____ Date _____ Instructor_____

Objectives:

In the first problem, you will practice using the timer OFF-delay function to create a PLC ladder logic diagram. In the second problem, you will practice using the retentive timer ON-delay function and counter function to create a PLC ladder logic diagram. You will verify the operation of both PLC ladder logic diagrams on your PLC lab station.

Equipment:

- ▶ Allen-Bradley fixed SLC 500 PLC or equivalent
- ▶ Single-pole, single-throw (SPST) switches (2)
- ▶ Normally open pushbuttons (2)
- ▶ Red, green, and white pilot lights
- ▶ Split-phase ac induction motor (fractional horsepower)

Procedure:

Activity 1

Using the PLC OFF-delay timer functions, draw the Allen-Bradley SLC 500 PLC ladder logic diagram that carries out the following sequence of events.

a. The black switch (SWB) is the master emergency switch that turns everything off.

b. When the thermostat (TSW) is closed, the red and white pilot lights turn on and the motor turns on.

c. When the thermostat (TSW) is opened, the motor turns off immediately and the red pilot light remains on for another 20 seconds. The white pilot light remains on for 40 seconds.

Name _____

Step 1. Draw the relay logic diagram for this circuit.

Step 2. Assign PLC input/output ports to the devices. Make the proper connections and program your PLC to carry out the logic diagrammed in Step 1.

Step 3. Use the Rockwell RSLogix 500 software to create the PLC ladder logic diagrams. Download the PLC ladder logic diagram into the PLC station. Place the PLC in the run/monitor mode.

Step 4. Demonstrate your working PLC system for your instructor. Approval: _____

Activity 2.

Using the PLC counter and retentive timer function, draw the relay logic diagram for a program that carries out the following sequence of events.

a. If the red pushbutton is pressed six times, the red light turns on.

b. If the green pushbutton is pressed three times, the green light turns on.

c. If the red pushbutton and the green pushbutton are pressed 12 times, only the white light turns on. Note that, as long as the total is 12, the white light should turn on. The combination does not matter.

d. Three timers should indicate how long each light has been on.

e. The black switch (SWB) is the master emergency switch that turns the entire circuit off.

Name _____

Step 1. Draw the relay logic diagram for this circuit.

Step 2. Assign PLC input/output ports to the devices. Make the proper connections and program your PLC to carry out the logic diagrammed in Step 1.

Step 3. Use the Rockwell RSLogix 500 software to create the PLC ladder logic diagrams. Download the PLC ladder logic diagram into the PLC station. Place the PLC in the run/monitor mode.

Step 4. Demonstrate your working PLC system for your instructor. Approval: _____

24-hour clock

Name _____ Date _____ Instructor_____

Objectives:

In this activity, you will use timer, counter, and move functions to create a 24-hour clock that can record up to three interruptions. Then, you will verify the operation of their PLC ladder logic diagram.

Equipment:

▶ Allen-Bradley fixed SLC 500 PLC or equivalent
▶ Single-pole, single-throw (SPST) switch
▶ Normally open pushbutton

Procedure:

Program your PLC lab station to build a clock. During a 24-hour period, you should be able to record the time (i.e., hours, minutes, and seconds) when the red pushbutton was pressed (signaling an emergency condition occurred). The program should be able to record up to three interruptions during a 24-hour period.

Name _____

Step 1. Draw the relay logic diagram for this circuit.

Step 2. Assign PLC input/output ports to the devices. Make the proper connections and program your PLC to carry out the logic diagrammed in Step 1.

Step 3. Use the Rockwell RSLogix 500 software to create the PLC ladder logic diagrams. Download the PLC ladder logic diagram into the PLC station. Place the PLC in the run/monitor mode.

Step 4. Demonstrate your working PLC system for your instructor. Approval: _____

Math and Compare Functions (1)

Name _____ Date _____ Instructor_____

Objectives:

In the first and second problems, you will create ladder diagrams to practice using math functions and compare functions. In the third problem, you will use add and compare functions to create a PLC ladder logic diagram. Then, you will verify the operation PLC ladder logic diagrams.

Equipment:

▶ Allen-Bradley fixed SLC 500 PLC or equivalent
▶ Normally open pushbuttons (2)
▶ Red, green, and white pilot lights
▶ Bell (6-volt)

Procedure:

Activity 1

Describe the following PLC math functions and provide an example for each.

Addition:

Subtraction:

Multiplication:

Division:

Name _____

Step 1. Assign PLC input/output ports to the devices. Make the proper connections and program your PLC to carry out the logic.

Step 2. Use the Rockwell RSLogix 500 software to create the PLC ladder logic diagrams. Download the PLC ladder logic diagram into the PLC station. Place the PLC in the run/monitor mode.

Step 3. Demonstrate your working PLC system for your instructor. Approval: _____

Activity 2

Describe the following PLC compare functions and provide an example for each.

Equal to (EQU):

Less than (LES):

Greater than (GRT):

Less than or equal to (LEQ):

Greater than or equal to (GEQ):

Step 1. Assign PLC input/output ports to the devices. Make the proper connections and program your PLC to carry out the logic.

Step 2. Use the Rockwell RSLogix 500 software to create the PLC ladder logic diagrams. Download the PLC ladder logic diagram into the PLC station. Place the PLC in the run/monitor mode.

Step 3. Demonstrate your working PLC system for your instructor. Approval: _____

Name _____

Activity 3

Program your PLC lab station to use two counters to count the pressing of two pushbuttons. Enable an add function and add the counter values together. If the sum is greater than 10, turn the green light on. If the sum is less than 10, turn the red light on. If the sum is equal to 10, sound the alarm and turn the white light on.

Step 1. Draw the relay logic diagram for this circuit.

Step 2. Assign PLC input/output ports to the devices. Make the proper connections and program your PLC to carry out the logic diagrammed in Step 1.

Step 3. Use the Rockwell RSLogix 500 software to create the PLC ladder logic diagrams. Download the PLC ladder logic diagram into the PLC station. Place the PLC in the run/monitor mode.

Step 4. Demonstrate your working PLC system for your instructor. Approval: _____

Math and Compare Functions (2)

Name _____ Date _____ Instructor_____

Objectives:

In this lab activity, basic math functions are used to solve two fundamental electrical equations. After solving the equations, compare functions are used to test the result and turn on the appropriate pilot light.

Equipment:

► Allen-Bradley fixed SLC 500 PLC or equivalent
► Single-pole, single-throw (SPST) switch
► Red and green pilot lights

Procedure:

Activity 1

In this problem, you will implement calculation of the following equation on your PLC lab station.

$$\frac{R1}{T1} = \frac{R2}{T2}$$

Where:

► R1 represents the resistance value for temperature t1
► R2 represents the resistance value for temperature t2
► T1 is temperature in degrees Kelvin: T1 = t1 + 273°
► T2 is temperature in degrees Kelvin: T2 = t2 + 273°

Assume that the variables R1, t1, and t2 are given. The PLC program should calculate R2. If R2 is greater than 100 ohms, the red light should turn on. If R2 is less than or equal to 100 ohms, the green light should turn on.

Name _____

Step 1. Draw the relay logic diagram for this circuit.

Step 2. Assign PLC input/output ports to the devices. Make the proper connections and program your PLC to carry out the logic diagrammed in Step 1.

Step 3. Use the Rockwell RSLogix 500 software to create the PLC ladder logic diagrams. Download the PLC ladder logic diagram into the PLC station. Place the PLC in the run/monitor mode.

Step 4. Demonstrate your working PLC system for your instructor. Approval: _____

Activity 2

In this problem, you will implement calculation of the following equation on your PLC lab station.

$$R = \rho \times (L/A)$$

Where:

- ρ is the resistivity of the material in ohm-meters. Let $\rho = 2$
- R represents the resistance value of the wire in ohms
- L is the length of the wire in meters (m)
- A is the area of the wire in meters squared (m^2)

Assume that variables ρ, L, and A are given. The PLC program should calculate R. If R is greater than or equal to 50 ohms, the red light turns on. If R is less than 50 ohms, the green light turns on.

Name _____

Step 1. Draw the relay logic diagram for this circuit.

Step 2. Assign PLC input/output ports to the devices. Make the proper connections and program your PLC to carry out the logic diagrammed in Step 1.

Step 3. Use the Rockwell RSLogix 500 software to create the PLC ladder logic diagrams. Download the PLC ladder logic diagram into the PLC station. Place the PLC in the run/monitor mode.

Step 4. Demonstrate your working PLC system for your instructor. Approval: _____

Math and Compare Functions (3)

Name _____ Date _____ Instructor _____

Objectives:

In the first problem, you will use multiply and divide functions to calculate results of multiplying and dividing the contents of two counter accumulated registers. In the second problem, you will use the add function to calculate the sum of the contents of two counter accumulated registers. In both problems, compare functions will be used to test the results and turn the appropriate output on.

Equipment:

▶ Allen-Bradley fixed SLC 500 PLC or equivalent
▶ Single-pole, single-throw (SPST) switch
▶ Normally open pushbuttons (2)
▶ Red, green, and white pilot lights
▶ Bell (6-volt)

Procedure:

Activity 1

In this problem, program the PLC lab station to operate as follows.

a. If the result of multiplying red and green pushbuttons is greater than or equal 18, all three lights turn on.

b. If the result of dividing the red pushbutton count by two is greater than 3, the bell sounds three times.

Name _____

Step 1. Draw the relay logic diagram for this circuit.

Step 2. Assign PLC input/output ports to the devices. Make the proper connections and program your PLC to carry out the logic diagrammed in Step 1.

Step 3. Use the Rockwell RSLogix 500 software to create the PLC ladder logic diagrams. Download the PLC ladder logic diagram into the PLC station. Place the PLC in the run/monitor mode.

Step 4. Demonstrate your working PLC system for your instructor. Approval: _____

Name _____

Activity 2

Use two counters to count the pressing of two pushbuttons. Enable an add function to add the counter values together. If the sum is greater than eight, the green light turns on. If the sum is less than eight, the red light turns on. If the sum is equal to eight, the alarm sounds and the white light turns on.

Step 1. Draw the relay logic diagram for this circuit.

Step 2. Assign PLC input/output ports to the devices. Make the proper connections and program your PLC to carry out the logic diagrammed in Step 1.

Step 3. Use the Rockwell RSLogix 500 software to create the PLC ladder logic diagrams. Download the PLC ladder logic diagram into the PLC station. Place the PLC in the run/monitor mode.

Step 4. Demonstrate your working PLC system for your instructor. Approval: _____

Name _____ Date _____ Instructor _____

Objectives:

In the first problem, compare functions are used to test the content of a counter accumulated register. A pilot light will turn on when the content is between two numbers. In the second problem, math functions are used to solve an equation that will convert unit dimensions.

Equipment:

- Allen-Bradley fixed SLC 500 PLC or equivalent
- Single-pole, single-throw (SPST) switches (2)
- Normally open pushbutton
- Green pilot light

Procedure:

Activity 1

In this problem, you will program the PLC to cause the green light to come on if the count from a pushbutton is either 10 or 15.

Step 1. Draw the relay logic diagram for this circuit.

Step 2. Assign PLC input/output ports to the devices. Make the proper connections and program your PLC to carry out the logic diagrammed in Step 1.

Step 3. Use the Rockwell RSLogix 500 software to create the PLC ladder logic diagrams. Download the PLC ladder logic diagram into the PLC station. Place the PLC in the run/monitor mode.

Step 4. Demonstrate your working PLC system for your instructor. Approval: _____

Activity 2

In this problem, you will design logic to perform unit conversions. Assume that you have an input that provides a dimension in inches and it is desired to have the dimensions displayed in feet and yards. Develop a PLC program to output all three dimensions. Use a counter to insert a number to verify the PLC circuit. For example, press a pushbutton fifty times. Then, three temporary registers must hold the numbers. Here, these numbers will be one yard, one foot, and two inches $((1 \times 3 \times 12) + (1 \times 12) + 2 = 36 + 12 + 2 = 50$ inches).

Step 1. Draw the relay logic diagram for this circuit.

Step 2. Assign PLC input/output ports to the devices. Make the proper connections and program your PLC to carry out the logic diagrammed in Step 1.

Step 3. Use the Rockwell RSLogix 500 software to create the PLC ladder logic diagrams. Download the PLC ladder logic diagram into the PLC station. Place the PLC in the run/monitor mode.

Step 4. Demonstrate your working PLC system for your instructor. Approval: _____

Math and Compare Functions (5)

Name _____ Date _____ Instructor _____

Objectives:

In the first problem, you will use add and subtract functions to calculate the results of adding and subtracting the content of accumulated counter registers. In the second problem, you will use multiply and divide functions to calculate results of multiplying and dividing the content of accumulated counter registers. In both problems, compare functions are used to test the results of the math functions. Appropriate pilot lights will turn on to demonstrate the results.

Equipment:

- Allen-Bradley fixed SLC 500 PLC or equivalent
- Single-pole, single-throw (SPST) switch
- Normally open pushbuttons (2)
- Bell (6-volt)
- Red, green, and white pilot lights

Procedure:

Activity 1

In this problem, program the PLC lab station to operate as follows.

a. When the total count from the red and green pushbuttons is equal to 10, only the red light turns on.

b. When the total count is between 10 and 15, only the green light turns on.

c. When the total count is greater than 15, only the white light turns on.

d. If the difference between the red and green pushbutton counts is greater than 6, the bell sounds continuously.

e. The black switch (SWB) is the master reset switch.

Name _____

Step 1. Draw the relay logic diagram for this circuit.

Step 2. Assign PLC input/output ports to the devices. Make the proper connections and program your PLC to carry out the logic diagrammed in Step 1.

Step 3. Use the Rockwell RSLogix 500 software to create the PLC ladder logic diagrams. Download the PLC ladder logic diagram into the PLC station. Place the PLC in the run/monitor mode.

Step 4. Demonstrate your working PLC system for your instructor. Approval: _____

Activity 2

In this problem, program the PLC lab station to operate as follows.

a. If the result of multiplying the red and green pushbuttons is greater than or equal to 18, all three lights turn on.

b. If the result of dividing the red pushbutton count by two is greater than three, the bell sounds three times.

c. The black switch (SWB) is the master reset switch.

Name _____

Step 1. Draw the relay logic diagram for this circuit.

Step 2. Assign PLC input/output ports to the devices. Make the proper connections and program your PLC to carry out the logic diagrammed in Step 1.

Step 3. Use the Rockwell RSLogix 500 software to create the PLC ladder logic diagrams. Download the PLC ladder logic diagram into the PLC station. Place the PLC in the run/monitor mode.

Step 4. Demonstrate your working PLC system for your instructor. Approval: _____

Shift Left and Shift Right Functions

Name _____ Date _____ Instructor _____

Objectives:

In this activity, you will learn how to use move, shift left (BSL), and shift right (BSR) functions to create PLC ladder logic diagrams. You will verify the operations of your PLC ladder logic diagrams on your PLC lab station.

Equipment:

- Allen-Bradley fixed SLC 500 PLC with 1747-L20A CPU or equivalent
- Single-pole, single-throw (SPST) switches (2)
- Normally open pushbuttons (2)
- Red, green, and white pilot lights

Procedure:

Activity 1

Describe the following PLC functions.

Move (MOV):

Bit shift left (BSL):

Name _____

Bit shift right (BSR):

Step 1. Draw a relay logic diagram for a circuit that uses all three functions.

Step 2. Assign PLC input/output ports to the devices. Make the proper connections and program your PLC to carry out the logic diagrammed in Step 1.

Step 3. Use the Rockwell RSLogix 500 software to create the PLC ladder logic diagrams. Download the PLC ladder logic diagram into the PLC station. Place the PLC in the run/monitor mode.

Step 4. Demonstrate your working PLC system for your instructor. Approval: _____

Name _____

Activity 2

In this problem, you will use move and bit shift right or bit shift left functions to turn the green, red, and white lights on every one second continuously. Only one light should be on at a time.

Step 1. Draw the relay logic diagram for this circuit.

Step 2. Assign PLC input/output ports to the devices. Make the proper connections and program your PLC to carry out the logic diagrammed in Step 1.

Step 3. Use the Rockwell RSLogix 500 software to create the PLC ladder logic diagrams. Download the PLC ladder logic diagram into the PLC station. Place the PLC in the run/monitor mode.

Step 4. Demonstrate your working PLC system for your instructor. Approval: _____

Jump and Master Control Reset Functions (1)

Name _____ Date _____ Instructor _____

Objectives:

In this activity, you will create PLC ladder logic diagrams that contain jump (JMP) and master control reset (MCR) functions. You will verify the operations of your PLC ladder logic diagrams on your PLC lab station.

Equipment:

- Allen-Bradley fixed SLC 500 PLC with 1747-L20A CPU or equivalent
- Single-pole, single-throw (SPST) switches (2)
- Bell (6-volt)
- Red, green, and white pilot lights
- Split-phase ac induction motor (2) (fractional horsepower)

Procedure:

Activity 1

In this problem, you will examine the jump and master control reset functions.

Step 1. Describe the following PLC functions and provide an example for each. Also, explain how the JMP function differs from the MCR function.

Jump (JMP):

Master control reset (MCR):

Name _____

Step 2. Assign PLC input/output ports to the devices. Make the proper connections and program your PLC to carry out the logic.

Step 3. Use the Rockwell RSLogix 500 software to create the PLC ladder logic diagrams. Download the PLC ladder logic diagram into the PLC station. Place the PLC in the run/monitor mode.

Step 4. Demonstrate your working PLC system for your instructor. Approval: _____

Activity 2

Design an MCR system to control the assembly line described in the following. All six stations are to function as set up by one of the two registers. A switch detects the presence of a part on the assembly line. Short and tall parts are sent down the line. Short parts get all six operations. The tall parts only get the first operation, the forth operation, the fifth operation, and the sixth operation. Tall parts are detected by a limit switch (use the thermostat switch on your PLC stations). This limit switch should activate the MCR function and seal it. After the sixth operation has been carried out, the MCR function should be unsealed and all the operations must turn off until another part is detected again.

Operations:	one	two	three	four	five	six
Pattern A (short):	1	1	1	1	1	1
Pattern B (tall):	1	0	0	1	1	1

Note that there should be two-second delays between the start of each operation. The operations are as follows.

One	Turn on motor number one.
Two	Turn on motor number two.
Three	Turn on the green light.
Four	Turn on the white light.
Five	Turn on the red light.
Six	Sound the bell.

Step 1. Draw the relay logic diagram for this circuit.

Step 2. Assign PLC input/output ports to the devices. Make the proper connections and program your PLC to carry out the logic diagrammed in Step 1.

Step 3. Use the Rockwell RSLogix 500 software to create the PLC ladder logic diagrams. Download the PLC ladder logic diagram into the PLC station. Place the PLC in the run/monitor mode.

Step 4. Demonstrate your working PLC system for your instructor. Approval: _____

Jump and Master Control Reset Functions (2)

Name _____ Date _____ Instructor _____

Objectives:

In this activity, two problems will further familiarize you with the use of jump (JMP) and master control reset (MCR) functions. You will verify the operations of your PLC ladder logic diagrams on your PLC lab station.

Equipment:

- Allen-Bradley fixed SLC 500 PLC with 1747-L20A CPU or equivalent
- Single-pole, single-throw (SPST) switches (2)
- Normally open pushbuttons (2)
- Bell (6-volt)
- Red, green, and white pilot lights
- Split-phase ac induction motors (2) (fractional horsepower)

Procedure:

Activity 1

In this problem, program the PLC lab station to operate as follows.

a. When the green pushbutton is pressed, motor one, motor two, and the white light turn on.

b. When the thermostat switch is closed and the green pushbutton is pressed, only the green light turns on.

Hint: Use the Jump function.

c. When the black switch is closed, the red light (only) blinks every one second, and the bell rings continuously.

Hint: Use the MCR function.

Name _____

Step 1. Draw the relay logic diagram for this circuit.

Step 2. Assign PLC input/output ports to the devices. Make the proper connections and program your PLC to carry out the logic diagrammed in Step 1.

Step 3. Use the Rockwell RSLogix 500 software to create the PLC ladder logic diagrams. Download the PLC ladder logic diagram into the PLC station. Place the PLC in the run/monitor mode.

Step 4. Demonstrate your working PLC system for your instructor. Approval: _____

Activity 2

In this problem, program the PLC lab station to operate as shown in the relay logic diagram of Figure 36-1.

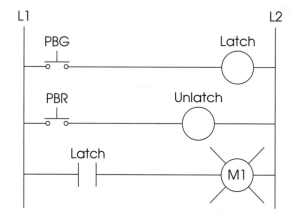

Figure 36-1

    a. Place a JMP function that can be activated by closing the thermostat switch. If the jump function is activated, the program will skip the *unlatch rung*.

    b. Place an MCR function that is controlled by the black switch.

Step 1. Draw the relay logic diagram for circuit shown in Figure 36-1.

Step 2. Assign PLC input/output ports to the devices. Make the proper connections and program your PLC to carry out the logic diagrammed in Step 1.

Step 3. Use the Rockwell RSLogix 500 software to create the PLC ladder logic diagrams. Download the PLC ladder logic diagram into the PLC station. Place the PLC in the run/monitor mode.

Step 4. Demonstrate your working PLC system for your instructor. Approval: _____

Subroutines

Name _____ Date _____ Instructor _____

Objectives:

In this activity, you will learn how to create subroutine files. You will create PLC ladder logic diagrams for main and subroutine files. Then, you will verify the operation of your PLC ladder logic diagrams on your PLC lab station.

Equipment:

- Allen-Bradley fixed SLC 500 PLC with 1747-L20A CPU or equivalent
- Single-pole, single-throw (SPST) switches (2)
- Normally open pushbuttons (2)
- Red and green pilot lights

Procedure:

Write a PLC program that has two subroutines. Turning on the black switch (SWB) activates the first subroutine. Thermostat (TSW) activates the second subroutine. In the first subroutine, press the green pushbutton (PBG) to turn on the green pilot light (Green_PLT). In the second subroutine, press the red pushbutton to turn on the red pilot light (Red_PLT).

Name _____

Step 1. Draw the relay logic diagram for this circuit.

Step 2. Assign PLC input/output ports to the devices. Make the proper connections and program your PLC to carry out the logic diagrammed in Step 1.

Step 3. Use the Rockwell RSLogix 500 software to create the PLC ladder logic diagrams. Download the PLC ladder logic diagram into the PLC station. Place the PLC in the run/monitor mode.

Step 4. Demonstrate your working PLC system for your instructor. Approval: _____

Sequencer Functions (1)

Name _____ Date _____ Instructor _____

Objectives:

In this activity, you will create a ladder logic diagram that utilizes the PLC sequencer output (SQO) function. You will verify the operation of your ladder logic diagram on your PLC lab station.

Equipment:

- Allen-Bradley fixed SLC 500 PLC with a 1747-L20A CPU or equivalent
- Single-pole, single-throw (SPST) switch
- Bell (6-volt)
- Red, green, and white pilot lights
- Split-phase ac induction motors (2) (fractional horsepower)

Procedure:

Use the sequencer function to place the following matrix in the PLC. Each of these steps should last two seconds. The process should continue until the master stop switch is opened.

Step Number	M1	M2	Green_PLT	Red_PLT	White_PLT	BELL
1	off	on	off	off	off	off
2	off	off	on	on	off	off
3	off	off	off	on	on	off
4	on	on	on	on	on	on
5	on	on	off	off	off	off
6	off	off	off	off	off	off

Name _____

Step 1. Draw the relay logic diagram for this circuit.

Step 2. Assign PLC input/output ports to the devices. Make the proper connections and program your PLC to carry out the logic diagrammed in Step 1.

Step 3. Use the Rockwell RSLogix 500 software to create the PLC ladder logic diagrams. Download the PLC ladder logic diagram into the PLC station. Place the PLC in the run/monitor mode.

Step 4. Demonstrate your working PLC system for your instructor. Approval: _____

Sequencer Functions (2)

Name _____ Date _____ Instructor _____

Objectives:

In this activity, you will program a sequencer output (SQO) function with variable time steps. Then, you will verify its operation on your PLC lab station.

Equipment:

- ▶ Allen-Bradley fixed SLC 500 PLC with 1747-L20A CPU or equivalent
- ▶ Single-pole, single-throw (SPST) switches (2)
- ▶ Red, green, and white pilot lights
- ▶ Split-phase ac induction motors (2) (fractional horsepower)

Procedure:

Use two sequencer and one timer function to operate the PLC lab station to perform the following sequence of events.

	Step 1	Step 2	Step 3	Step 4
Event:	Run motor one	Turn on red and green lights	Run both motors	Turn on the white light
Duration:	2 seconds	2.5 seconds	3.25 seconds	1.5 seconds

Black switch (SWB) starts the process, and thermostat (TSW) is utilized as a reset switch.

Step 1. Draw the relay logic diagram for this circuit.

Step 2. Assign PLC input/output ports to the devices. Make the proper connections and program your PLC to carry out the logic diagrammed in Step 1.

Step 3. Use the Rockwell RSLogix 500 software to create the PLC ladder logic diagrams. Download the PLC ladder logic diagram into the PLC station. Place the PLC in the run/monitor mode.

Step 4. Demonstrate your working PLC system for your instructor. Approval: _____

Sequencer Functions (3)

Name _____ Date _____ Instructor_____

Objectives:

In this activity, two problems will further familiarize you with the use of sequencer output (SQO) functions in PLC ladder logic diagrams. You will verify the operation of your PLC ladder logic diagrams on your PLC lab station.

Equipment:

▶ Allen-Bradley fixed SLC 500 PLC with 1747 L20A CPU or equivalent
▶ Single-pole, single-throw (SPST) switch
▶ Normally open pushbutton
▶ Red, green, and white pilot lights
▶ Bell (6-volt)
▶ Split-phase ac induction motors (2) (fractional horsepower)

Procedure:

Activity 1

Use the sequencer functions to create an operation scheme for an industrial washer. The six operating steps and the delay time between the steps are as follows.

    a. Energize the soap release solenoid (turn the green light on) for four seconds.

    b. Open the input valve for hot water (turn the white light on) for five seconds.

    c. Operate the washer impeller (turn motor number one on) for twelve seconds.

    d. Open the drain water valve (ring the bell).

    e. Turn on the drain pump (turn on motor number two) for three seconds.

    f. Turn on the heat element during the drying cycle (turn on the red light) for six seconds.

Name _____

Step 1. Draw the relay logic diagram for this circuit.

Step 2. Assign PLC input/output ports to the devices. Make the proper connections and program your PLC to carry out the logic diagrammed in Step 1.

Step 3. Use the Rockwell RSLogix 500 software to create the PLC ladder logic diagrams. Download the PLC ladder logic diagram into the PLC station. Place the PLC in the run/monitor mode.

Step 4. Demonstrate your working PLC system for your instructor. Approval: _____

Activity 2

Use the sequencer functions to perform the following steps when a green pushbutton is pressed:

a. Turn the green light on, wait four seconds, then go to Step 2.

b. Turn the white light on, wait five seconds, then go to Step 3.

c. Turn on motor number one for twelve seconds, turn it off, then go to Step 4.

d. Turn on motor number two for eight seconds and then go to Step 5.

Note: Make sure that a reset switch is included in the program.

Name _____

Step 1. Draw the relay logic diagram for this circuit.

Step 2. Assign PLC input/output ports to the devices. Make the proper connections and program your PLC to carry out the logic diagrammed in Step 1.

Step 3. Use the Rockwell RSLogix 500 software to create the PLC ladder logic diagrams. Download the PLC ladder logic diagram into the PLC station. Place the PLC in the run/monitor mode.

Step 4. Demonstrate your working PLC system for your instructor. Approval: _____

CPLCPLCPLCPLCPLCPLCPL
PLCPLCPLCPLCPLCPLCP
CPLCPLCPLCPLCPLCPLCPL
PLCPLCPLCPLCPLCPLCP
CPLCPLCPLCPLCPLCPLCPL
PLCPLCPLCPLCPLCPLCP

Lab
Assignment

Sequencer Functions (4) 41

Name _____ Date _____ Instructor _____

Objectives:

In the first problem, you will use a sequencer output (SQO) function that has fixed times between its operating steps. In the second problem, you will use a sequencer output (SQO) function that has variable times between its operating steps. You will test both ladder logic diagrams on your PLC lab station.

Equipment:

▶ Allen-Bradley fixed SLC 500 PLC with 1747-L20A CPU or equivalent
▶ Single-pole, single-throw (SPST) switch
▶ Red, green, and white pilot lights
▶ Split-phase ac induction motors (2) (fractional horsepower)

Procedure:

Activity 1

Use the sequencer function to program the PLC to control a traffic light. The green light should stay on for 30 seconds. The yellow light should stay on for five seconds. Finally, the red light should stay on for 20 seconds. The process should continue until the master stop switch is opened.

Step 1. Draw the relay logic diagram for this circuit.

Step 2. Assign PLC input/output ports to the devices. Make the proper connections and program your PLC to carry out the logic diagrammed in Step 1.

Step 3. Use the Rockwell RSLogix 500 software to create the PLC ladder logic diagrams. Download the PLC ladder logic diagram into the PLC station. Place the PLC in the run/monitor mode.

Step 4. Demonstrate your working PLC system for your instructor. Approval: _____

Activity 2

Use the sequencer function to place the following matrix in the PLC. Each step should last three seconds. The process should continue until the master stop switch is opened.

Step Number	M1	M2	Green_PLT	Red_PLT	White_PLT
1	on	on	off	off	off
2	off	off	on	on	off
3	off	off	off	on	on

Step 1. Draw the relay logic diagram for this circuit.

Step 2. Assign PLC input/output ports to the devices. Make the proper connections and program your PLC to carry out the logic diagrammed in Step 1.

Step 3. Use the Rockwell RSLogix 500 software to create the PLC ladder logic diagrams. Download the PLC ladder logic diagram into the PLC station. Place the PLC in the run/monitor mode.

Step 4. Demonstrate your working PLC system for your instructor. Approval: _____

PLC Local Area Network (1)

Name _____ Date _____ Instructor _____

Name _____

Name _____

Name _____

Objectives:

In this activity, you will connect two PLC slave stations to one PLC master station. You will then assign nodes to these PLC stations. Using the Who Active function, you will make sure that the computer is at node zero, the master PLC is at node three and slave PLCs are at nodes one and two. You will create three PLC ladder logic diagrams, download them to the appropriate PLC, and verify the operation of the PLC networked system. You will also learn how to use the Message Read function in the master PLC ladder logic diagram.

Equipment:

- ▶ Allen-Bradley SLC 503 PLC or equivalent
- ▶ Allen-Bradley fixed SLC 500 PLCs or equivalent (2)
- ▶ Single-pole, single-throw (SPST) switches (5)
- ▶ Normally open pushbuttons (2)
- ▶ Pilot lights (3 red, 3 green)

Procedure:

For this lab assignment, connect three PLC stations in a local area network. Then, program the PLC network systems as stated in the following paragraphs.

a. The master PLC program will have two message functions.

b. When the green pushbutton on the master PLC station is pressed, it should use a latch function to go to the first message function. This message function reads the status of the timers and counters that are on slave PLC station #1. Press the red pushbutton in order to unlatch and exit the message function.

The green light indicates that the PLC is servicing message function #1.

c. When the black switch on the master PLC station is closed, it should use a latch function to go to the second message function. This message function reads the status of the timers and counters that are on slave PLC station #2. Press the red pushbutton in order to unlatch and exit the message function.

The red light indicates that the PLC is servicing message function #2.

d. The red pushbutton is used to unlatch the input bits B3/0 and B3/1.

e. All the data gathered by the master PLC station should reside in memory locations N7:0, N7:1, …. of the master PLC.

    f. Each individual slave PLC station should have a program that will continuously implement the following tasks:

The green light is on for five seconds while the red light is off.

The red light is on for eight seconds while the green light is off.

Step 1. Draw the relay logic diagram for this circuit.

    Master PLC station:

    Slave PLC station #1:

Slave PLC station #2:

Step 2. Assign PLC input/output ports to the devices. Make the proper connections and program your PLC to carry out the logic diagrammed in Step 1.

Step 3. Use the Rockwell RSLogix 500 software to create the PLC ladder logic diagrams. Download the PLC ladder logic diagram into the PLC station. Place the PLC in the run/monitor mode.

Step 4. Demonstrate your working PLC system for your instructor. Approval: _____

Name _____ Date _____ Instructor _____

Name _____

Name _____

Name _____

Objectives:

In this activity, you will modify the master PLC ladder logic diagram created in the previous lab assignment. You will add two Message Write functions to the master PLC ladder logic diagram. Then, you will verify the operation of your PLC networked system.

Equipment:

▶ Allen-Bradley SLC 503 PLC or equivalent

▶ Allen-Bradley fixed SLC 500 PLCs or equivalent (2)

▶ Single-pole, single-throw (SPST) switches (6)

▶ Normally open pushbuttons (2)

▶ Pilot lights (3 red, 3 green)

Procedure:

Modify the master PLC stations specified for the PLC network in Lab Assignment #42 as follows. Add Message Write functions in order to be able to vary the time duration for which the red lights and the green lights on the slave PLC stations stay on. Note that, two Message Write functions in each message function are needed. Each Message Write is used for changing one time delay on the slave PLC sequencer. There are a total of six message functions in the master PLC program. There are one Message Read and two Message Write functions for each slave PLC.

Name _____

Step 1. Draw the relay logic diagram for this circuit.

     Master PLC station:

     Slave PLC station #1:

Name _____

Slave PLC station #2:

Step 2. Assign PLC input/output ports to the devices. Make the proper connections and program your PLC to carry out the logic diagrammed in Step 1.

Step 3. Use the Rockwell RSLogix 500 software to create the PLC ladder logic diagrams. Download the PLC ladder logic diagram into the PLC station. Place the PLC in the run/monitor mode.

Step 4. Demonstrate your working PLC system for your instructor. Approval: _____

Name _____ Date _____ Instructor_____

Name _____

Name _____

Name _____

Objectives:

In this activity, you will modify the master PLC ladder logic diagram used in the previous two lab assignments. You will add two Message Write functions to the master PLC ladder logic diagram. Then, you will verify the operation of the PLC networked system.

Equipment:

▶ Allen-Bradley SLC 503 PLC or equivalent
▶ Allen-Bradley fixed SLC 500 PLCs or equivalent (2)
▶ Single-pole, single-throw (SPST) switches (6)
▶ Normally open pushbuttons (2)
▶ Pilot lights (3 red, 3 green)

Procedure:

Modify the master PLC stations specified for the PLC network in Lab Assignments #42 and #43 as follows. Add two more Message Write functions in order to be able to synchronize the operations of the slave PLC stations. Use the previous PLC program to synchronize the operation of the slave PLC stations once every two minutes.

Name _____

Step 1. Draw the relay logic diagram for this circuit.

    Master PLC station:

Slave PLC station #1:

Slave PLC station #2:

Name _____

Step 2. Assign PLC input/output ports to the devices. Make the proper connections and program your PLC to carry out the logic diagrammed in Step 1.

Step 3. Use the Rockwell RSLogix 500 software to create the PLC ladder logic diagrams. Download the PLC ladder logic diagram into the PLC station. Place the PLC in the run/monitor mode.

Step 4. Demonstrate your working PLC system for your instructor. Approval: _____